GRIEF♦SHARE®

YOUR
JOURNEY FROM
MOURNING TO JOY

For more information, contact
Church Initiative
250 S. Allen Rd.
P.O. Box 1739
Wake Forest, NC 27588-1739

Phone: 1-800-395-5755 (US and Canada);
919-562-2112 (Local and international)
Fax: 919-562-2114
Email: info@churchinitiative.org
Web address: www.churchinitiative.org, www.griefshare.org

CONTENTS

GriefShare Sessions:
Each session includes a note-taking outline for the video, daily From Mourning to Joy exercises and a Weekly Journal.

ABOUT GRIEFSHARE

GRIEFSHARE IS A NETWORK OF THOUSANDS OF GRIEF RECOVERY SUPPORT GROUPS MEETING AROUND THE WORLD. GRIEFSHARE IS A PROGRAM WITH DIRECTION AND PURPOSE. WITH GRIEFSHARE YOU WILL LEARN HOW TO WALK THE JOURNEY OF GRIEF AND BE SUPPORTED ON THE WAY. IT IS A PLACE WHERE HURTING PEOPLE FIND HEALING AND HOPE.

David and Nancy Guthrie, co-hosts of the GriefShare videos, have faced the deaths of two of their three children. Since the publication of Nancy's book, *Holding On to Hope*, David and Nancy have continued to share what they've learned with grieving people through the Respite Retreats they hold for couples who have lost children, through speaking around the country and through their books, including *When Your Family's Lost a Loved One*. David, Nancy and their son, Matt, live in Nashville, Tennessee, where David publishes children's music for the church through his company, Little Big Stuff Music.

HELP FOR HURTING PEOPLE

Listed below is information about other care group resources from Church Initiative, which publishes GriefShare. For further information, call 1-800-395-5755 (US and Canada) or 919-562-2112 (local and international), visit our website at www.churchinitiative.org or email us at info@churchinitiative.org.

www.divorcecare.org
DivorceCare is a seminar/small group resource to help people who are hurting because of separation and divorce.

www.dc4k.org
DC4K is designed to bring healing to children of divorce and to give them hope and the tools to develop healthier relationships within their own families.

www.beforeyoudivorce.org
Before You Divorce is a marriage crisis intervention tool. It is designed to help prevent divorce and save families.

www.facingforever.org
Facing Forever is a fascinating study of the issues of life, death and eternity. It is an excellent small group discipleship and evangelism program.

www.singleandparenting.org
Single & Parenting addresses the unique challenges faced by single parents, offering support, instruction and hope.

FOR MORE INFORMATION
www.churchinitiative.org

HOW GRIEFSHARE WORKS

YOUR GRIEFSHARE GROUP IS DESIGNED TO HELP YOU RECOVER FROM THE DEEP HURT OF LOSS. YOUR GRIEFSHARE EXPERIENCE INCLUDES THREE KEY ELEMENTS THAT WORK TOGETHER TO GUIDE YOUR HEALING PROCESS. WE ENCOURAGE YOU TO COMMIT TO TAKING PART IN ALL THREE ASPECTS OF GRIEFSHARE.

❶ Video seminar

- At each session you will view a video featuring personal stories of people like you who are grieving the death of a loved one, and expert insights on topics important to grief recovery. As you watch the videos, expect to discover new ways of understanding what is happening to you. Changing the way you think about your situation is crucial for healing from grief. We recommend you use the video outlines in this workbook to take notes while viewing the seminars.

- The video seminars open with mini-dramas portraying what it's like to live with grief; this will help you become more aware of your own grief process.

- Additional DVD material is available for those desiring in-depth information on specific topics. Your GriefShare leader will share information with you about its availability.

- For those whose children are dealing with grief, a GriefShare for Kids video will offer suggestions and help answer tough questions you may have in caring for the children. See your GriefShare leader to arrange a showing of this material.

> "WHEN INDIVIDUALS WRITE OR TALK ABOUT PERSONALLY UPSETTING EXPERIENCES, SIGNIFICANT HEALTH IMPROVEMENTS HAVE BEEN FOUND."[*]

❷ Support group

- After the video you will become part of a small support group to discuss what you've seen on the video and what's going on in group members' lives. You'll stay with the same group of people for the 13 GriefShare sessions. It's likely that you will begin to see the people in your group as "family."

- Your group leaders will have discussion questions to help guide the group time. It's also important to take time to "catch up" on the trials, problems and successes experienced by members between sessions. Sharing your experiences

---

[*] James W. Pennebaker, Emmanuelle Zech and Bernard Rime. 2002. Disclosing and Sharing Emotion: Psychological, Social, and Health Consequences. In *Handbook of Bereavement Research*, eds. Margaret S. Stroebe, Robert O. Hansson, Wolfgang Stroebe and Hank Schut (Washington, DC: American Psychological Association, 2002), 533.

will help you organize and clarify your thoughts on what is happening to you and allow others to understand how they can help you along your journey of grief.

- Each week your group will take time to discuss the daily From Mourning to Joy workbook exercises and how they have helped you throughout the week.

❸ Workbook

- From Mourning to Joy exercises: The heartfelt daily prayers, meaningful reflections, questions and Scripture verses will comfort and strengthen you on your grief journey. You will be encouraged to have a fresh look at what God says about grief. Completing the exercises can make a real difference in your recovery, and we encourage you to spend time each day on them.

- My Weekly Journal: The Weekly Journal pages provide you with prompts and questions for you to focus your writing on. Journaling your thoughts, questions, fears, hopes and losses can be a tremendous asset in helping you process your grief. We encourage you to get a separate notebook to write in. Set aside time every week to write in your journal.

- Care Cards: In the back, you'll find 13 Care Cards. Tear out a perforated card each week and place it where you will see it often throughout each day.

- The Foundation for Healing describes how you can build your life on the firm foundation of Jesus Christ.

- "How to Write a Grief Letter": Learn how to help your friends help you (p. 23).

- The article "Are You Expecting Too Much from Your Comforters?" will help you have reasonable expectations of those who comfort you (p. 90).

- The Thank You and Invitation Cards are perforated postcards in the back of your workbook that you can fill out and send to friends and/or your church leaders.

- Help Center: See page ix for further GriefShare resources, available both online and in print, including free daily email encouragements you can sign up for.

 If you're active in a church, turn there for support during this difficult time. If you're not, you are missing out on a key element to your healing. Talk with your group leaders about how finding a church can help you. God doesn't expect you to carry the whole load by yourself. He uses the church and the people in it to help in your recovery.

WE'VE SEEN GRIEFSHARE HELP PEOPLE IN GRIEF HEAL AND DEVELOP HOPE FOR THE FUTURE. WE ENCOURAGE YOU TO BECOME COMMITTED TO YOUR GRIEFSHARE GROUP AND TO LOOK EXPECTANTLY AT WHAT GOD CAN DO IN YOUR LIFE!

GROUP GUIDELINES

Each group will develop its own rules and guidelines, but here are some broad suggestions about how to be an effective group member.

Maintain confidentiality:

Don't talk about things you hear in the group to people outside the group. This will help develop an atmosphere of trust. (Keep in mind, there is no way the group can guarantee confidentiality, so use discretion about what you share.)

Share:

There is no requirement that you talk or share in the group, but you are encouraged to do so!

Be sensitive:

Some of you are naturally outgoing and comfortable sharing your feelings. Some of you are a bit shy. If you are outgoing, make sure you don't dominate the group. If you tend to be quiet or shy, make an effort to participate (you'll be glad you did).

Test your expectations:

This is a group designed to help you and the other group members heal from the hurt of grief. For those who have lost a mate, it is not an environment to encourage dating relationships (as you'll see on the videos, dating too early can add to your hurt!). You and the other group members are emotionally vulnerable. It's important to build mutual trust, demonstrating that you are part of this group to find healing.

Be well mannered:

Take care to protect the integrity of the GriefShare program as well as each group member. Please make every effort to avoid speaking of others in disparaging terms.

Help Center

WE ARE ALWAYS GLAD TO HELP. THAT'S WHY WE DESIGNED THESE RESOURCES. TAKE A MOMENT TO FAMILIARIZE YOURSELF WITH EACH ONE, BECAUSE YOU WILL BE BETTER EQUIPPED TO MAKE THE JOURNEY OF GRIEF IF YOU KNOW WHAT HELP IS AVAILABLE. VISIT WWW.GRIEFSHARE.ORG, EMAIL INFO@GRIEFSHARE.ORG OR CALL US AT 800-395-5755 (919-562-2112 INTERNATIONAL) WITH ANY QUESTIONS YOU MAY HAVE ABOUT THE GRIEFSHARE RESOURCES.

Through a Season of Grief book

This book of 365 short, daily messages is based on the GriefShare program. Each day you will be equipped with biblical comfort and practical teaching to help you take steps forward toward healing. Look for *Through a Season of Grief* by Bill Dunn and Kathy Leonard at www.griefshare.org or at your local bookstore.

A Season of Grief FREE daily email messages

The *Through a Season of Grief* book is available online in the form of daily email messages you can sign up for at www.griefshare.org. You can also email a friend who is hurting and encourage him or her to sign up.

Find a group

Moving to a new town? Have a friend or relative who could be helped by a GriefShare group? GriefShare groups are meeting throughout the US, Canada and several other countries. To find groups in other areas, search our database at www.griefshare.org and enter a zip code, area code, city or country. You can also call us at 800-395-5755.

GriefShare CDs & Downloadable Audio Files

With a set of GriefShare CDs or the downloadable audio files, you can catch up on sessions you missed or find encouragement by listening to your favorite programs. You can also gift the audio version of GriefShare to others. You'll receive the audio tracks from each of the 13 GriefShare sessions. To order, call 800-395-5755 or visit www.griefshare.org.

Online bookstore

We know it can be difficult to find reliable resources to help you heal. Our online bookstore, accessed through www.griefshare.org, includes books that are reviewed and selected based on the value they will bring to your life and the healing process.

Tell a friend

The GriefShare website, www.griefshare.org, includes a link to tell a friend about this site. If you know someone hurting because of loss, make sure he or she knows about GriefShare by having this email invitation sent recommending the GriefShare site.

Other GriefShare website helps

At www.griefshare.org, print and use the Help for the Journey personal Bible study, read The Foundation for Healing pages and learn more about the GriefShare program.

Surviving the Holidays website

At www.griefshare.org/holidays find articles, real-life stories and video clips to help you reduce stress, minimize loneliness and discover a healthy approach to the holiday season after the death of your loved one. Ask your GriefShare leader about the possibility of a special Surviving the Holidays two-hour seminar prior to the holidays.

THE FOUNDATION FOR HEALING

A personal relationship with Jesus Christ

THROUGHOUT THE GRIEFSHARE PROGRAM, YOU WILL HEAR PEOPLE TALKING ABOUT THE IMPORTANCE OF A RELATIONSHIP WITH JESUS CHRIST IN HEALING FROM THE DEEP PAIN OF GRIEF. IN FACT, YOU WILL HEAR IT SAID THAT YOU CANNOT FULLY HEAL FROM GRIEF WITHOUT THE POWER OF CHRIST IN YOUR LIFE.

Please read the information on these pages carefully. It will show you how to have a relationship with Jesus Christ and how this relationship can make a real difference in your life as you heal from your loss.

What is at the center of your life?

You tend to "orbit" around certain people, things or events in your life. They are the relationships, possessions and circumstances you value most. They give meaning to life and bring joy to you.

Here are some examples:

Husband or wife
Job
Children
Financial resources
Favorite activities
Houses, cars and possessions
Friends
Health

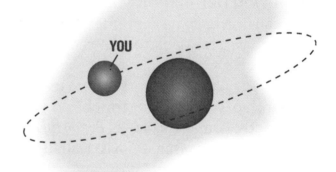

Take a minute and list the people or things that your life revolves around. It may be one thing or a combination of items.

_____

_____

_____

How solid is your center?

In our solar system, planets have a predictable orbit because the sun is a stable gravitational "center." Imagine what would happen to those planets if the sun suddenly disappeared.

Now look at your list comprising the things at the center of your life. Which are permanent (cannot disappear or be lost)?

_____

_____

_____

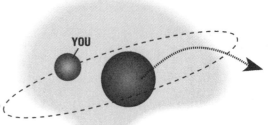

Most things in your life can disappear. A husband or wife can leave the marriage or die. Your financial conditions can change suddenly. Possessions break, rust and wear out. Your health can deteriorate. When these things happen, your "orbit" will disappear as well, sending your life into an emotional tumble.

In the end, only one thing is permanent. Your relationship with God, if you have one, cannot be taken away. Because this relationship with God is so critical to your stability, it's important to know for sure that you have the kind of relationship with Him that will ensure He is permanently in the center of your life.

Achieving permanent stability

How can God become the center of your life? The first step is to remove a major barrier between you and Him.

The Bible says that our sins separate us from having a relationship with God. Sin is disobeying God's written commands. Romans 3:23 says, *For all have sinned and fall short of the glory of God.* It also says that the result of sin is death (separation from God). *For the wages of sin is death, but the free gift of God is eternal life in Christ Jesus our Lord* (Romans 6:23 NASB).

Your sin keeps you from God. Many people try to "earn" a relationship with Him by "being a good person" and "doing good things." But notice in the verse above that eternal life is a gift. It cannot be earned. You must receive it from the Giver. *For it is by grace you have been saved, through faith—and this not from yourselves, it is the gift of God—not by works, so that no one can boast* (Ephesians 2:8–9).

Breaking through the barrier

If you can't overcome your sin and earn a relationship with God, how can He become the center of your life? The Bible says that Jesus Christ removed the barrier between God and you by dying in your place. He paid the price for your disobedience. Romans 5:8 puts it this way: *But God demonstrates his own love for us in this: While we were still sinners, Christ died for us.* It's also important to realize that Jesus Christ is the only way to a relationship with

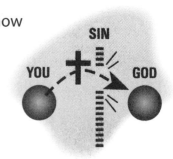

God. John 14:6 reads, *Jesus answered, "I am the way and the truth and the life. No one comes to the Father except through me."*

Making it real in your life

Maybe right now you ache for the stability, security and wholeness that come from having God at the center of your life. Once He's there, you can access His power to help you heal from your grief. He can help stabilize your life's orbit.

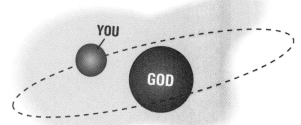

The first step is to believe that Jesus is God's only Son. There is no other Savior. You cannot get to God except through Him. If you believe in Him, you can act on that faith. He can stabilize your life's orbit.

How can God become the center of your life?

The Bible says that each person must receive Jesus as personal Lord and Savior through faith. To do this, you must first realize that you are a sinner and repent of (turn away from) your sin. The Bible says, *They should repent and turn to God and prove their repentance by their deeds* (Acts 26:20).

Receiving Jesus through faith means trusting Him alone as the payment for your sin and surrendering your life to Him. *If you confess with your mouth, "Jesus is Lord," and believe in your heart that God raised him from the dead, you will be saved. For it is with your heart that you believe and are justified, and it is with your mouth that you confess and are saved* (Romans 10:9–10).

Taking the step

If you would like to surrender your life to Jesus Christ, here is a prayer you can pray. Why not do it right now?

> Dear Lord,
>
> I know I have done things that are wrong. Please forgive me for these sins.
> I invite Jesus Christ into my life as my Savior and Lord.
> As my Savior, I ask You to save me from the effect of my sins.
> As my Lord, I receive You as the center of my life and give You control of it.
> Thank you for forgiving my sin and giving me the gift of eternal life with You.
>
> In Jesus' name I pray,
> Amen

God's promise to people who invite Christ into their lives is described in 1 John 5:11–13: *And this is the testimony: God has given us eternal life, and this life is in his Son. He who has the Son has life; he who does not have the Son of God does not have life. I write these things to you who believe in the name of the Son of God so that you may know that you have eternal life.*

THE BIBLE SAYS YOUR RELATIONSHIP WITH GOD THROUGH JESUS CHRIST CAN NEVER BE TAKEN FROM YOU.

My sheep listen to my voice; I know them, and they follow me. I give them eternal life, and they shall never perish; no one can snatch them out of my hand. My Father, who has given them to me, is greater than all; no one can snatch them out of my Father's hand (John 10:27–29).

THINGS REALLY ARE DIFFERENT NOW

If you invited Christ into your life, many things have changed. Look at what has happened.

Christ is in your life:
I have been crucified with Christ and I no longer live, but Christ lives in me. The life I live in the body, I live by faith in the Son of God, who loved me and gave himself for me (Galatians 2:20).

Christ's power is in your life:
I can do all things through Him who strengthens me (Philippians 4:13 NASB).

Your sins were forgiven:
In him we have redemption through his blood, the forgiveness of sins, in accordance with the riches of God's grace (Ephesians 1:7).

You became a permanent part of God's kingdom:
Therefore, since we are receiving a kingdom that cannot be shaken, let us be thankful, and so worship God acceptably with reverence and awe (Hebrews 12:28).

You received the gift of eternal life:
For God so loved the world that he gave his one and only Son, that whoever believes in him shall not perish but have eternal life (John 3:16).

You can find abundant life now:
The thief comes only to steal, and kill, and destroy; I came that they may have life, and have it abundantly (John 10:10 NASB).

You can find God's peace:
Do not be anxious about anything, but in everything, by prayer and petition, with thanksgiving, present your requests to God. And the peace of God, which transcends all understanding, will guard your hearts and your minds in Christ Jesus (Philippians 4:6–7).

WHAT'S NEXT?

Inviting Jesus into your life is only the first step in an exciting relationship with God. You'll want to get to know Him better and learn His plan for your life.

If you have just asked Jesus into your life, let your pastor, counselor or a mature Christian friend know. He or she can help you grow even closer to God. A good way to learn more about Jesus Christ is to read the book of John, found in the New Testament of the Bible. We suggest you commit to reading a chapter of this exciting book each day. As you read, pray that you will gain an even better understanding of how Jesus is changing your life.

SURVIVING THE HOLIDAYS
WHEN YOU ARE GRIEVING

Visit our special website to find practical information about surviving the holidays while you grieve.

www.griefshare.org/holidays

GRIEFSHARE EXPERTS

 **Susan K. Beeney, R.N.**, author and featured speaker for grief and loss, is the founder and executive director of New Hope Grief Support Community in southern California. New Hope is committed to providing grief education and training, grief support groups for all ages, and camps for kids who have suffered the death of a loved one.

 **Sabrina D. Black** is an international speaker and professional counselor. She is the CEO and clinical director of Abundant Life Counseling Center in Detroit, Michigan, and has authored/co-authored several books, including *Counseling in African American Communities*. She has experienced the loss of her uncle, sister-in-law and father-in-law and the miscarriage of her baby.

 **Judith Blore**, director of BASIS, a ministry of Handi*Vangelism, provides help for bereaved parents and their families in southeastern Pennsylvania. Judith has experienced the death of her mother, who was also a bereaved parent.

 **Dee Brestin**, of Women's Friendship Ministries, is a conference speaker and the author of many Bible study guides and books for women, including *Falling in Love with Jesus*, *Living in Love with Jesus* and *The Friendships of Women*. She lost her husband to cancer.

The late **Dr. Bill Bright** was the founder and president of Campus Crusade for Christ. For over 50 years he dedicated his life to helping people find new  life and hope through a relationship with Christ.

 **Rev. Noel Castellanos** is the CEO of the Christian Community Development Association (CCDA), a nonprofit organization that teaches people in poor communities how to rebuild from a place of devastation into a place of hope. He is also the founder of the Latino Leadership Foundation and La Villita Community Church in Chicago, Illinois.

 **Dr. Sahara Chea** is the vice chair of the National Cambodian Presbyterian Council and serves as a New Church Development pastor for the First Cambodian Presbyterian Ministry in Tacoma, Washington. Dr. Chea survived the Cambodian killing fields and witnessed the horrific deaths of many of his people. Today he shares Christ's message of forgiveness, comfort and freedom.

 **Dr. Tim Clinton** is the president of the executive board for the American Association of Christian Counselors. He is a professor of counseling and pastoral care at Liberty University and the executive director of the Liberty University Center for Counseling and Family Studies. He has authored *Caring for People God's Way: Personal and Emotional Issues, Addictions, Grief, and Trauma* and other books. Dr. Clinton has experienced the loss of his father.

Dr. Jim Conway is the author of numerous books, a conference speaker and the president of Midlife Dimensions. He also ministers to people through radio, television, and telephone and letter counseling. He served as a pastor for almost 30 years. Dr. Conway has experienced the death of his wife.

Dr. Larry Crabb is a psychologist, conference speaker, Bible teacher and author. He is the founder and director of New-Way Ministries. Dr. Crabb is the Spiritual Director for the AACC. His books include *Shattered Dreams* and *The Safest Place on Earth*. He has experienced the death of his brother.

Dr. Robert C. De Vries and **Dr. Susan Zonnebelt-Smeenge** have both experienced the loss of a spouse. Now remarried to each other, they work together to help people in grief. Dr. De Vries is professor emeritus of church education at Calvin Theological Seminary. He was married to his first wife for 28 years before she died of cancer. Dr. Zonnebelt-Smeenge is a Licensed Clinical Psychologist at Pine Rest Christian Mental Health Services. Her first husband was diagnosed with a malignant brain tumor when he was 32 and died 18 years later. They are speakers and joint authors of several books and articles, including *Getting to the Other Side of Grief: Overcoming the Loss of a Spouse*, *The Empty Chair: Handling Grief on Holidays and Special Occasions*, *Living Fully in the Shadow of Death: Assurance and Guidance to Finish Well* and *Traveling Through Grief: Learning to Live Again After the Death of a Loved One*.

Joni Eareckson Tada is an author, artist, broadcaster and the founder and president of Joni and Friends Ministries. Her books and worldwide ministry reflect her experience of God's love and grace since becoming a quadriplegic as a result of a diving accident over 35 years ago. Her books include *Heaven* and *When God Weeps*.

Elisabeth Elliot was born of missionary parents in Brussels, Belgium, and served as a missionary in Ecuador where her husband, Jim Elliot, was killed by the Auca Indians in 1956. She also experienced the death of her second husband. She is a speaker and the author of several books, including *A Path through Suffering*, *Facing the Death of Someone You Love* and *The Path of Loneliness*.

Dr. Michael R. Emlet is a counselor and faculty member at the Christian Counseling and Educational Foundation (CCEF) and a lecturer in practical theology at Westminster Theological Seminary. He holds graduate degrees from the University of Pennsylvania and Westminster Theological Seminary. He worked as a family physician for 12 years before joining CCEF.

Anne Graham Lotz is a speaker and the president of AnGeL Ministries. The daughter of Billy and Ruth Graham, Anne hosts *Just Give Me Jesus* revivals throughout the world. Her books include *Why? Trusting God When You Don't Understand* and *Heaven: My Father's House*.

Dr. Jack Hayford is the founding pastor of The Church on the Way in Van Nuys, California. He has authored more than three dozen books and has written over 600 songs. He is also the founder and chancellor of The King's College and Seminary in Van Nuys. Dr. Hayford has experienced the loss of his sister and his parents.

The late **Dr. E. V. Hill** was recognized as one of the greatest preachers in the world. He was the pastor at Mt. Zion Missionary Baptist Church in Los Angeles for over 40 years. Dr. Hill experienced the death of his wife.

Dr. Robert Jeffress serves as pastor of the First Baptist Church of Dallas, Texas. He has written several books, including *When Forgiveness Doesn't Make Sense*, and hosts the television program *Pathway to Victory*. His mother has passed away.

The late **Barbara Johnson**, who had lost two sons and her husband, was involved in grief ministry. A humorous writer and speaker, she was head of Spatula Ministries in La Habra, California, supporting parents who lost children through death or estrangement. Her many books include *Laughter from Heaven*, *Splashes of Joy in the Cesspools of Life* and *God's Most Precious Jewels Are Crystallized Tears*.

Dr. Robert W. Kellemen is a licensed professional clinical counselor and the director of the Biblical Counseling and Spiritual Formation Network of the AACC. He is also the author of *God's Healing for Life's Losses*. On his 21st birthday, he experienced his father's death.

Dr. Tim Lane is the president of CCEF in Glenside, Pennsylvania. He had served as a pastor for 10 years and is co-author of *How People Change* and *Relationships: A Mess Worth Making* and the author of the booklets *Forgiving Others* and *Conflict*. His younger brother died at 42 after a 25-year struggle with addictions.

Susan Lutz served as a counselor at CCEF for 14 years. Now she counsels at her church, where her husband serves as pastor. She has authored the booklet *Thankfulness: Even When It Hurts*. Susan has experienced the loss of both parents.

Dr. Erwin Lutzer is the senior pastor of the Moody Church in Chicago, Illinois. He has written over 30 books and is the featured speaker on three radio programs heard on Christian stations nationwide: *The Moody Church Hour*, *Songs in the Night* and *Running to Win*. He has experienced the loss of his granddaughter, who was stillborn.

Bruce Marchiano is a professional actor who, having given his life to the Lord in 1989, had the privilege of portraying Jesus in the Visual Bible film production *The Gospel of Matthew*. Known for his joyous and passionate portrayal of the Savior, Bruce now travels the world sharing the Savior and his experiences as an actor portraying Him.

Janet Paschal, a talented singer and songwriter, served as the official spokesperson of the Mission of Mercy, an international Christian relief organization. She has received Grammy nominations and is a popular conference speaker and frequent guest on Christian radio and television talk shows. Janet lost her grandfather.

Dr. Norman Peart is the founder and pastor of Grace Bible Fellowship, a nondenominational, multicultural church in Cary, North Carolina. He is also a professor at the University of North Carolina. Dr. Peart has experienced the loss of his grandmother.

Lorraine Peterson, author of *Restore My Soul*, has been a teacher in the United States and in American schools in Ecuador and Mexico. Lorraine currently resides in Mexico, where she works with young people and also ministers to people who have experienced the death of a loved one. Lorraine has experienced the death of her mother and stepmother.

Dr. James Petty is the executive director of the Children's Jubilee Fund in Philadelphia, Pennsylvania, which provides scholarships for low-income, inner-city students to attend Christian schools. Dr. Petty is a counselor, author and former pastor. He received his degree from Westminster Theological Seminary.

Dr. David Powlison, editor of The *Journal of Biblical Counseling*, is a counselor and faculty member at CCEF. He serves as an adjunct professor of practical theology at Westminster Theological Seminary and is the author of *Speaking Truth in Love: Counsel in Community*, *Seeing with New Eyes: Counseling and the Human Condition Through the Lens of Scripture* and *Power Encounters*.

Dr. Ray Pritchard is the president of Keep Believing Ministries. He is a conference speaker and frequent guest on Christian radio and television programs. Dr. Pritchard has ministered extensively overseas, preaching in India, Nepal, Paraguay, Columbia, Haiti, Nigeria, Russia and Belize. He has authored several books, including *The Healing Power of Forgiveness*, *Discovering God's Will for Your Life* and *Why Did This Happen to Me?* He has experienced his father's death.

Lois M. Rabey is a speaker and writer. She has authored several books, including *When Your Soul Aches* and *Moments for Those Who Have Lost a Loved One*. Lois lost her husband in a hot-air balloon ride accident.

Dr. Quincy Scott, Jr., is the dean of the Thomas J. Boyd Chapel at Shaw University. He is a retired army chaplain, having pastored soldiers and their families for 27 years. Dr. Scott has a Masters Degree in Counseling. His doctoral thesis written at Howard University is "Ministry to Terminal Children and their Families." He has done grief work throughout his years in the military but most especially during the Vietnam Era. He has experienced the death of his father.

 **Winston T. Smith** is the director of counseling and a faculty member at CCEF, and a lecturer in practical theology at Westminster Theological Seminary. He holds a Master of Divinity degree from Westminster Theological Seminary, where he is also in the process of attaining a Doctor of Ministry degree. His areas of interest and experience include marriage and family, depression and anxiety.

 **Dr. Joseph Stowell** was the president of the Moody Bible Institute of Chicago for 18 years and is the current president of Cornerstone University in Grand Rapids, Michigan. Dr. Stowell is an internationally recognized speaker and a bestselling author.

 **Dr. Siang-Yang Tan** is a professor of psychology at Fuller Theological Seminary. His areas of expertise include helping people cope with anxiety, anger and depression. He has authored many publications, including *Lay Counseling, Full Service: Moving from Self-Serve Christianity to Total Servanthood*, *Rest* and *Coping with Depression* with John Ortberg. He is the senior pastor of First Evangelical Church Glendale in California. He has experienced the death of his father.

 **Sissi Tran** is a licensed marriage/family therapist in Kern County, California. As a mental health clinician, she works with high school students in special education. She has experience facilitating grief/bereavement support groups for a local hospice. She has experienced separation from her family in the Vietnam War, and the loss of her father to illness and her aunt to leukemia.

 **Dr. John Trent** is a nationally recognized author and speaker. He is the president of Strong-Families and The Center for StrongFamilies out of Scottsdale, Arizona. These ministries are dedicated to strengthening marriage and family relationships worldwide. Dr. Trent has experienced the loss of his mother and father.

 **Dr. Paul David Tripp** is the president of Paul Tripp Ministries and the author of several books on practical issues of Christian living, including *A Shelter in the Time of Storm*. He is on the pastoral staff of Tenth Presbyterian Church in Philadelphia and has been a counselor for many years. He has experienced his father's death.

 **Dr. Edward T. Welch** is a counselor and faculty member at CCEF and a professor of practical theology at Westminster Theological Seminary. He has authored several books, including *Depression: A Stubborn Darkness*, and he speaks at conferences and other venues. His father passed away.

 H. Norman Wright is a grief therapist and certified trauma specialist. He is the author of over 70 books, including *Experiencing Grief, Recovering from Losses in Life, It's Okay to Cry, Reflections of a Grieving Spouse* and *The New Guide to Crisis and Trauma Counseling*. He is on the faculty of Talbot Graduate School of Theology and on the executive board of the American Association of Christian Counselors. He has received honorary doctorates from Western Conservative Baptist Seminary and Biola University. He has experienced the death of his wife and son.

Ravi Zacharias, president of Atlanta-based Ravi Zacharias International Ministries, was born in India and immigrated to Canada in 1966. He received his Master of Divinity from Trinity International University in Deerfield, Illinois. He has written several books, has lectured in more than 50 countries and has a weekly radio program, *Let My People Think*. Mr. Zacharias has been honored by the conferring of a Doctor of Divinity degree both from Houghton College, New York, and from Tyndale College and Seminary, Toronto, and a Doctor of Laws degree from Asbury College in Kentucky.

Zig Ziglar, is a motivational speaker and the author of 27 books, including *Confessions of a Grieving Christian*, which is based on the grief journey he experienced after the loss of his daughter Suzan. He is chair of the Zig Ziglar Corporation, whose mission is to equip people to utilize their physical, mental and spiritual resources.

LIVING WITH GRIEF

Grief is disruptive and disorienting. What's worse is that some people will make you feel like you are overreacting to the death of your loved one. Your GriefShare experience will include three key components that make up each session:

1. Video seminar

2. Group discussion

3. Workbook and journaling exercises

These three elements are critical parts of your healing process. They will introduce you to others who've made it through grief. They offer suggestions to help you endure your season of grief. Completing each will help you find answers to the following questions:

- Is it okay for me to grieve?
- How long will my grief last?
- How do I deal with these overwhelming emotions?
- How should I handle the big decisions that need to be made?

EXPECT GOD TO SHOW YOU THAT THERE IS HOPE.

Video Outline
Use this outline to write down important concepts, encouraging words or questions you may have while viewing the video.

What Is Grief?
Grief is a maddening experience

You are not going crazy

Grief is the recognition you've lost someone you love

Grief Is Normal
It's not a sign of weakness

Pretending you're okay isn't helpful

Jesus' grief is instructive

Give yourself permission to grieve

Many men don't permit themselves to grieve

Honestly express your emotions

Expect your pain to come and go

We Are Often Unprepared for Grief
Many people avoid thinking about death

You may be surprised at how long it lasts

You may be thinking about suicide

Eventually, life will get better

Suggestions for Living with Grief
Lean into your grief

Follow the ABC's of grief

ABC'S OF GRIEF
A - Always be true to yourself
B - Believe you'll make it
   Believe God's Word
C - Remember people Care
   Communicate your needs

Postpone big decisions

Don't rush into remarriage

Dealing with people who rush you

What to do when you can't

Do the next thing

Commit to this GriefShare group

Use your GriefShare workbook

"EVEN THOUGH YOUR HEART IS BREAKING AND TEARS ARE CLOUDING YOUR EYES AND STAINING YOUR CHEEKS, GOD DOES GIVE US SOMETHING WORTH TRUSTING IN TOUGH TIMES. AND THAT'S HIM, AND HIM ALONE."
—DR. JOSEPH STOWELL

IN OUR NEXT SESSION
The Journey of Grief

Grief is like a journey, and this next session will help prepare you for what to expect along the way.

GriefShare online ➡ www.griefshare.org

Find a GriefShare group

Have a friend or family member in another city who needs a GriefShare group?

Our online search engine helps you find the nearest group!

FREE daily email encouragement messages

Sign up for "A Season of Grief." Receive an uplifting email message each day for a year.

GriefShare online bookstore

Helpful grief recovery books at discount prices. Find books written by experts from the GriefShare DVDs and other professionals.

ON THE VIDEOS YOU HEARD OTHER PEOPLE SHARE THEIR EXPERIENCES IN GRIEF. THIS SECTION GIVES YOU THE OPPORTUNITY TO THINK THROUGH YOUR OWN GRIEF EXPERIENCE.

As you complete the exercises, you will begin to …

■ realize you are never alone in your grief
■ learn about the true source of peace
■ find out why it is important to allow yourself to grieve
■ discover what God's character has to do with your grief

Take time each day and complete these exercises to learn more about how to live with grief. Also, be sure to write in the Weekly Journal section at the end of each From Mourning to Joy section.

The presence of pain, and the presence of God

God's Word to You

"My bones are in agony. My soul is in anguish. How long, O LORD, how long?" (Psalm 6:2–3)

How would you describe your pain?

As you learned on the video, it takes longer to heal than most people imagine. What concerns or issues does this raise in your mind regarding your situation?

Remember

Grief is a natural part of life. The feelings you have are normal. Other people are experiencing these same feelings.

And though it may seem like God has abandoned you, He is there for you. You are never alone.

Talking to God
God, the pain of my grief is pressing in on all sides, and sometimes I can't breathe with the force of it. Lift me into Your arms. Comfort me with Your presence, and teach me to grieve.

In Your Life
What hope or comfort did you have from listening to the people on the GriefShare video?

Even while you are living with grief, you can have the living God dwelling within you.* How is this (or how might this be) comforting?

Is He living inside you? If not, would you like that?

* If you would like more information about how God can live within a person, see The Foundation for Healing section on page xi.

The source of peace

God's Word to You
"Now may the Lord of peace himself give you peace at all times and in every way. The Lord be with all of you." (2 Thessalonians 3:16)

Who is the source of peace?

The writer of 2 Thessalonians 3:16 (see previous page) says God can give you peace in all situations. What will it take for you to experience peace again?

What do you think it means to experience peace "in every way"?

Remember

A person who is filled with peace may still be overcome with emotions of grief. These overwhelming emotions occur because you loved the person you lost.

You can have peace in the midst of your whirling, confusing emotions. Keep going back to the Source of Peace.

Talking to God

God, I am blindsided by my emotions and bewildered. You say that You give peace at all times and in every way. I need Your peace in my pain.

In Your Life

When a person is grieving, it's common for him or her to want the pain to go away without seeking the unique peace God offers. Have you been more motivated to get rid of your pain or to obtain peace? Why?

What would be different if, while living with grief, you gained a deeper sense of God's peace?

Grieving leads to comfort

God's Word to You

"Blessed are those who mourn, for they will be comforted." (Matthew 5:4)

What does Jesus promise will happen to those who mourn/grieve?

Are you allowing yourself to grieve? Why or why not?

What does your grieving look like?

Remember

You are not grieving only one loss. The loss of your loved one brings layers of losses that must be acknowledged and mourned. Honest grieving leads to comfort.

Talking to God

God, I am dragged down by new losses every day. Help me to recognize all I have lost so I may mourn and then experience Your comfort. I need to be honest about my feelings.

In Your Life

Each day you may discover new losses that have occurred as a result of the loss of your loved one. Identifying and mourning these losses is an important part of healing. Here are ideas of new losses you may be facing. Check any that apply:

☐ Job   ☐ Source of laughter
☐ Home   ☐ Cuddler
☐ Possessions   ☐ Cook
☐ Relationships   ☐ Mechanic
☐ Companion   ☐ Gardener
☐ Confidant   ☐ Shoulder to cry on
☐ Lover   ☐ Walking partner

What else is on your list? Each week you will be able to update your list in your Weekly Journal (at the end of each From Mourning to Joy section).

Take time to talk with God about each of these losses.

What does God's comfort look like? Where do you find it?

God's Word to You

"Find rest, O my soul, in God alone; my hope comes from him. He alone is my rock and my salvation; he is my fortress, I will not be shaken." (Psalm 62:5–6)

The author of this passage describes what he finds in God and who God is. List everything you can learn about God's character from the verses above.

Getting to know God's character will aid you in receiving His comfort. What attributes of God from Psalm 62:5–6 do you find most comforting?

Remember

Grief can cloud your vision and keep you from seeing the comfort and hope that is available for you.

Dr. Paul David Tripp says in order to receive God's comfort, you have to place yourself where His comfort is. Find it in prayer and the Bible, in time spent with Christians, in His creation, under the mentoring of a mature Christian, in God-pleasing music, in quiet time spent with God. Your GriefShare group is a great place to stay connected to God's comfort!

Talking to God

God, I know my pain isn't going to just disappear, so please show me what Your comfort looks like. Teach me to cling to Your comfort and to the hope that is found in You.

In Your Life

In the last couple of weeks, what have you found comfort in?

God has provided many resources of comfort, including inspirational music, people, your GriefShare group, Bible truths, church and much more. Which resources will you make a commitment to be faithful to, even on days you don't feel like it?

DAY 5

God is close to you (the brokenhearted)

God's Word to You

"The LORD is close to the brokenhearted and saves those who are crushed in spirit." (Psalm 34:18)

During your journey of grief, when have you felt closest to God?

At what moments have you felt farthest away from God? Why do you think this is?

Remember

As strong as your feelings are, you cannot let them determine what is truth. If you are a brokenhearted child of God, He is close to you.

Talking to God

God, my spirit is crushed, and my heart is broken. Sometimes I can't feel You, but I know You are here. I choose truth over feelings. Save me, Faithful God.

In Your Life

What do you do when you can't feel God's presence?

How can you be sure that He is always by your side, always faithful to love you?

Psalm 34:18 says God "saves those who are crushed in spirit." What do you think you need to be saved from?

GriefShare online ➡ www.griefshare.org

Find a GriefShare group

Have a friend or family member in another city who needs a GriefShare group?

Our online search engine helps you find the nearest group!

FREE daily email encouragement messages

Sign up for "A Season of Grief." Receive an uplifting email message each day for a year.

GriefShare online bookstore

Helpful grief recovery books at discount prices. Find books written by experts from the GriefShare DVDs and other professionals.

My Weekly Journal

Living with Grief

1. The loss of a loved one results in layers of losses that are uncovered as you travel your grief journey; for instance, the loss of dreams, relationships, possessions, time, duties and around-the-house helps (such as cook, mechanic or gardener).

The newest loss I have felt is …

The most significant losses I have experienced are …

2. Personal evaluation: How are you feeling this week?

	Really Bad	Okay	Pretty Good	Great
Emotionally				
Physically				
Spiritually				
Relationally				

3. Choose one (or more) of the following ideas to journal on:

a. From the moment you wake up until you crawl into bed at night, what is it like to live with grief?

b. The unknowns of grief can create anxiety and fear. Write a prayer to God telling Him what you are afraid of and asking for His help in overcoming those fears.

c. What are some differences in the way you are grieving compared with other people?

d. Describe a big decision you are facing now and your feelings about the different options. What do you think God would think of those options?

e. Making a commitment to do anything right now may seem overwhelming. We urge you to write a commitment to stick with this GriefShare group and to attempt to complete the workbook exercises.

We encourage you to use a separate notebook for your weekly journaling.

THE JOURNEY OF GRIEF

Since the death of your loved one, you've started a journey. It's not a trip you planned, but it's a trip you must take. This week's video, discussion time and workbook exercises will help you understand what to expect along the way.

As you complete this session, you'll begin to discover answers to the following questions:

- Where is God in all this?
- Why do I feel so alone?
- Why is this pain so intense and immobilizing?
- Am I taking too long to grieve?

EXPECT GOD TO SHOW YOU THAT HE IS WITH YOU ON THIS JOURNEY OF GRIEF.

Video Outline
Use this outline to write down important concepts, encouraging words or questions you may have while viewing the video.

Your Journey of Grief Is Unique
Your grief won't resemble others'

> "BE WHOEVER YOU ARE. YOUR OWN PATTERN OF GRIEF WILL BE YOUR PATTERN OF GRIEF."
> —DR. LARRY CRABB

What helps you won't help others

Don't question your love for the one you've lost

What Shapes Your Journey of Grief?
Your relationship shapes your journey

The amount of time spent grieving before a loved one dies shapes your journey

Your efforts to heal shape your journey

Complete the five tasks of grief

Your Journey of Grief Can Seem Unending
Don't rush through grief

Dealing with those who try and rush your grief

Your Loss Is Deeper Than You Thought
You've lost more than your loved one

How to inventory your losses

"PEOPLE AROUND YOU DON'T UNDERSTAND GRIEF UNLESS THEY'VE BEEN THROUGH IT THEMSELVES."
—H. NORMAN WRIGHT

Grief affects you when you least expect it

What you should do when ambushed in the presence of others

Grief Affects Your Relationships
You may be too tired for your friends

You may be overwhelmed by well-meaning friends

You may need to write a grief letter to your friends
(See page 23 for instructions on how to write a grief letter and for sample letters)

You may need help writing and distributing your grief letter

Frequently Asked Questions about the Journey of Grief
Will this pain ever end?

Will my life ever return to normal?

Does a new normal mean forgetting?

What should I do with belongings?

IN OUR NEXT SESSION
The Effects of Grief

You will begin to understand which reactions to the death of a loved one are normal, and which are not.

ON THE VIDEOS, YOU MET SEVERAL PEOPLE WHO HAVE TRAVELED THE JOURNEY OF GRIEF BEFORE YOU AND WHO CAN RELATE TO YOUR DEEP PAIN.

By completing this week's workbook exercises, you will start to …

- learn the value of bringing your questions to God
- be assured of the goodness of God and His unchanging character
- examine grief's effects on you
- let yourself grieve in your own way

Move forward on your journey by making a commitment to complete the workbook exercises and write in your Weekly Journal each week.

Questioning God; feeling He has abandoned you

God's Word to You
"My God, my God, why have you forsaken me?" (Psalm 22:1)

Do you feel that God has abandoned you? If so, how has that feeling impacted you?

Think about your life. Recall and list examples of how God has been present in your life.

Why is it good to ask God questions that are worrying you?

Remember

Questioning God during grief is not an expression of doubt or a sin. Don't hesitate to ask God to help you make sense of how a good God would allow bad things to happen.

Talking to God

God, I don't get it. Why did You let this happen? If You say You love us so much, why would You allow this? What am I missing here? Help me to reconcile what I know is true about You with my experience.

In Your Life

What questions do you have for God?

List some resources (people, books, support groups, etc.) that will help you find answers to your questions.

God never changes

God's Word to You

"Jesus Christ is the same yesterday and today and forever." (Hebrews 13:8)

We know from the Bible that Jesus is God. For you, what is the significance of God's unchanging character?

How can an unchanging God help you handle the biggest challenge you are facing?

Remember

During grief, there are two things you can be sure of. One, your emotions will change. And two, God won't. He has always been there for you; He is here for you now; and He will never leave you. Go to Him.

Talking to God

Lord God, nothing has been the same since that day. I often don't know if I'm about to cry or crumble. Every step I take is uncertain. Please carry me.

In Your Life

One change you may face is the changing attitudes of people around you who are trying to "help" you. Sometimes they will be patient and caring; other times they will seem to be rushing you through your grief. If this happens, why will it be important to remember that God does not change?

GriefShare
devotional book

Available at local bookstores, online bookstores and directly from GriefShare at **www.griefshare.org**.

GriefShare CDs & Downloadable Audio Files

Take GriefShare with you

Listen to GriefShare in your car, at home or wherever you go. Catch up on sessions you missed or listen to your favorite sessions again. You'll receive the audio tracks from each of the 13 GriefShare sessions. Order at **www.griefshare.org**.

How grief affects you

God's Word to You

"Be merciful to me, O LORD, for I am in distress; my eyes grow weak with sorrow, my soul and my body with grief." (Psalm 31:9)

How is grief affecting you physically and emotionally?

How is grief affecting your spiritual life?

Remember

Grief affects every aspect of your life. Remember to take care of your body as well as your soul. You have to put effort into the healing/grieving process, even if it's only one small step at a time.

Talking to God

God, sometimes I feel overwhelmed and unable to function. With Your strength, I can take small steps forward every day. Give me the strength to tend to all my needs—emotional, spiritual and physical, and give me the courage and humility to ask for help as often as I need it.

In Your Life

How has grief affected your relationships with others?

What steps have you taken to continue moving forward on your grief journey?

Take time to grieve

God's Word to You
"There is a time for everything, and a season for every activity under heaven: a time to be born and a time to die … a time to weep and a time to laugh, a time to mourn and a time to dance." (Ecclesiastes 3:1–2, 4)

What "time" is it in your life?

How does the above verse provide comfort?

Remember
It's important to take the time you need to grieve. If your current situation does not afford you the freedom to grieve the way you need to, schedule time to cry out to the Lord.

Talking to God
God, I want the pain to stop. Give me the wisdom to take all the time I need to grieve the loss of my loved one.

In Your Life
What feelings cause you to want to rush through your grief?

What obstacles are preventing you from expressing your grief?

When and where would be a good time and location for you to freely express your emotions out loud to God each day?

Created in God's image

God's Word to You

"So God created man in his own image, in the image of God he created him; male and female he created them." (Genesis 1:27)

"Jesus wept." (John 11:35)

Are you reflecting God's image (likeness) on your grief journey? How?

When you grieve, in what ways is your grief different from that of others?

Remember

The Bible says we are created in God's image. But because all people are created to be different, we each reflect God in unique ways, and that includes the way we grieve.*

If you are moving toward God, you can be assured that you are displaying God's image and that you are on the path of healing.

Talking to God

God, my relationship with You and the relationship I had with my loved one are one-of-a-kind. When I worry that I'm grieving the wrong way, help me understand that I don't need to be anyone but the person You created me to be.

In Your Life

When others trivialize your grief, how does it help you to remember that Jesus, God the Son, grieved the death of his friend Lazarus?

In what areas of your life are you trying to do things on your own, without God?

* Insights on Gen. 1:27 inspired by GriefShare expert Susan Lutz.

MY WEEKLY JOURNAL

The Journey of Grief

1. The loss of a loved one results in layers of losses that are uncovered as you travel your grief journey; for instance, the loss of dreams, relationships, possessions, time, duties and around-the-house helps (such as cook, mechanic or gardener).

The newest loss I have felt is …

The most significant losses I have experienced are …

2. Personal evaluation: How are you feeling this week?

	Really Bad	Okay	Pretty Good	Great
Emotionally				
Physically				
Spiritually				
Relationally				

3. Choose one (or more) of the following ideas to journal on:

a. Tell about a time when you felt that the way you were grieving was "wrong" because it was different from how others were grieving.

b. Write a "grief letter" to your family and friends explaining what they can do or say that would be helpful and not hurtful to you. (See page 23 for instructions on how to write this letter and for sample letters.)

c. If your typical reaction to your daily grief is to "stuff" your pain, describe what that looks like. Then, write a prayer asking God to help you honestly express your emotions.

d. Some people believe that emotions of grief come in predictable stages: after one emotion is finished, then comes the next. Explain why you know that's not true.

e. When you come to the point in your journey where you need to make decisions about your loved one's belongings, what ideas do you have of things you could do with those belongings that would honor God and your loved one?

We encourage you to use a separate notebook for your weekly journaling.

HOW TO WRITE A GRIEF LETTER

ONE REASON GRIEF CAN BE SO PAINFUL IS THAT THE PEOPLE YOU EXPECT TO UNDERSTAND AND COMFORT YOU ARE THOSE RUSHING YOU THROUGH GRIEF.

People sometimes say hurtful words in their attempts to help. Other times they wear you out with their "kind" questions—you often end up repeating the same emotionally draining responses over and over again to different people throughout your day. Other friends may barge in and try to take over the task of your healing: "You need to do this, eat this, read this, go here, go there."

A helpful suggestion by H. Norman Wright is to write your friends a grief letter. While you may feel awkward giving someone a grief letter, this will help ease the stress of your situation.

How to write a grief letter to your friends:

1. Describe what you have experienced and how you are feeling about it.

2. Let people know what they can expect from you in your current state.

3. Give your friends instructions on what they can do to help during this time. Let them know what is needed and when it is needed.

Give this letter to everyone you know. The people who receive the letter will appreciate knowing how they can better help you, and you will have less stress and more appropriate help suited to your unique grieving style.

If you don't have energy to write, ask someone to help. Specify what you want written and have that person pass it out.

How to Write a Grief Letter

H. Norman Wright shares this sample grief letter in his book, *Recovering from Losses in Life* (Revell, 2006):

Dear Friend (family, pastor, fellow workers …)

Recently I have suffered a devastating loss. I am grieving and it will take months and even years to recover from this loss.

I wanted to let you know that I will cry from time to time. I don't apologize for my tears since they are not a sign of weakness or a lack of faith. They are God's gift to me to express the extent of my loss, and they are also a sign that I am recovering.

At times you may see me angry for no apparent reason. Sometimes I'm not sure why. All I know is that my emotions are intense because of my grief. If I don't always make sense to you, please be forgiving and patient with me. And if I repeat myself again and again, please accept this as normal.

More than anything else I need your understanding and your presence. You don't always have to know what to say or even say anything if you don't know how to respond. Your presence and a touch or hug lets me know you care. Please don't wait for me to call you since sometimes I am too tired or tearful to do so.

If I tend to withdraw from you, please don't let me do that. I need you to reach out to me for several months.

Pray for me that I would come to see meaning in my loss someday and that I would know God's comfort and love. It does help to let me know that you are praying for me.

If you have experienced a similar type of loss, please feel free to share it with me. It will help rather than cause me to feel worse. And don't stop sharing if I begin to cry. It's all right, and any tears you express as we talk are all right too.

This loss is so painful, and right now it feels like the worst thing that could ever happen to me. But I will survive and eventually recover. I cling to that knowledge, even though there have been times when I didn't feel it. I know that I will not always feel as I do now. Laughter and joy will emerge once again someday.

Thank you for caring about me. Thank you for listening and praying. Your concern comforts me and is a gift for which I will always be thankful.

HOW TO WRITE A GRIEF LETTER

Dear Friends,

This last year has been far more difficult than I could have ever imagined. I now realize this process of grieving is messy, and it lasts a lot longer than I had anticipated. Thank you for being my friend and supporting me during this season of grief.

I would so appreciate your prayers for my family and myself.

Your presence and understanding means so very much. You don't have to know what to say or even say anything ... just a caring glance, a warm hug, or a listening ear speak volumes to my heart. Please don't wait for me to call, since a lot of the time I feel too tired. When I withdraw, please don't let me do that for too long. If you are up for an early morning walk, give me a call. I'm not full of energy, but even a short walk seems to help.

Please know I don't need fixing ... that is God's job! Your love, patience and prayers will sustain me through this time. God is faithful; He is my sustaining grace.

Please pray that God will use this time of grieving to grow me and equip me to minister to others with greater compassion than ever before. I know I will not just survive ... joy will return! Pray this will happen soon! Thank you for caring enough to read this letter. I covet your prayers.

In Christ,
Nancy

HOW TO WRITE A GRIEF LETTER

Here are a few things to remember as you write your grief letter:

■ Trying to anticipate and include everything you'll need during your journey of grief makes writing a grief letter difficult. Share what you need right now. As you work through your grief, your needs will change. When they do, you can send out a different grief letter to your friends and family.

■ People won't be offended if you tell them exactly how to help you. They will appreciate your clear instructions. (For them, it takes the guesswork out of serving you.)

■ If you don't tell people what you need, you run the risk of not being cared for and/or receiving unwanted assistance. As you probably discovered, during the journey of grief unwanted assistance can be a burden.

DON'T PUT OFF WRITING YOUR GRIEF LETTER.
START YOURS TODAY!

THE EFFECTS OF GRIEF

T HE EMOTIONAL, SPIRITUAL, PHYSICAL AND MENTAL EFFECTS OF GRIEF MAY HAVE YOU WONDERING IF YOU'RE GOING CRAZY. REST ASSURED, THIS IS PROBABLY NOT THE CASE. THIS WEEK'S VIDEO WILL HELP YOU UNDERSTAND WHAT SOME OF THE MOST COMMON REACTIONS TO GRIEF ARE. THE DISCUSSION TIME WILL ALLOW YOU TO HEAR HOW OTHERS ARE BEING AFFECTED BY GRIEF. AND THE WORKBOOK EXERCISES WILL HELP YOU DISCOVER HOW GOD CAN HELP YOU WHEN YOU FEEL HELPLESS.

As you complete the parts of this session, you'll uncover the answers to these questions:

- Am I losing my mind?
- While grieving, what unique temptations do I need to be on guard for?
- Is it wise for me to isolate myself from others?

> EXPECT GOD TO SHOW YOU IF YOU ARE EXPRESSING YOUR GRIEF
> IN A WAY THAT IS DOING YOU HARM.

Video Outline
Use this outline to write down important concepts, encouraging words or questions you may have while viewing the video.

Common Responses to Death of Loved One
Denial

> "WE'VE GOT TO BE
> WILLING TO BE WEAK."
> —DR. PAUL DAVID TRIPP

Questioning your sanity

Memory loss

Hallucinations

Physical problems

    Monitor your health

Tangled emotions

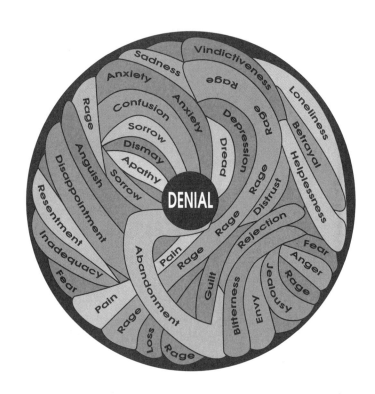

Anger with loved one

Anger with God

Relief and joy

    "WHEN THE DUST OF MY TROUBLE SETTLES, GOD IS STANDING THERE NEXT TO ME, AND HE HAS DUST ON HIS SHOULDERS BECAUSE HE'S BEEN THERE ALL ALONG." —DR. PAUL DAVID TRIPP

Drawing closer to God

Questioning the value of faith

Finding Relief from Grief
Comfort yourself

Look at memorabilia

Journal

> "GENUINE HEALING FROM
> GRIEF COMES NOT IN AN
> ARTIFICIAL CLIMATE—
> ACTIVITY, DRUGS OR
> WHATEVER—IT COMES
> THROUGH THE REALITY OF
> KNOWING JESUS CHRIST."
> —DR. JOHN TRENT

Don't numb your pain

Suicide isn't the answer

IN OUR NEXT SESSION
When Your Spouse Dies

In Session 4 we'll explore what happens when your spouse dies. If your loss is some-one other than a spouse, please plan to still attend. Much of the biblical teaching and expert insights on grief can be applied to all situations. Attending this session will also help you connect with the friends you are making in your GriefShare group.

YOU CAN PROBABLY RELATE TO THE "TANGLED BALL OF EMOTIONS" AND "ROLLER-COASTER EMOTIONS" YOU WERE INTRODUCED TO ON THE VIDEO. IN THIS WEEK'S WORKBOOK EXERCISES YOU WILL BE INTRODUCED TO SOME STRATEGIES TO HELP YOU PERSEVERE THROUGH THE MOST DIFFICULT TIMES. YOU WILL BEGIN TO ...

- identify and untangle your many emotions
- find tools to help when you are tempted to give up or numb your pain
- think about where God is and how He can help you
- discover how your feelings can skew your perception of what is truth

If you are struggling to find the time to do these exercises, ask God to show you a brief time each day to fit in the questions and the Weekly Journal. This is important for your healing.

Overwhelming, unpredictable emotions

God's Word to You

"How long must I wrestle with my thoughts and every day have sorrow in my heart?" (Psalm 13:2)

What thoughts and emotions do you wrestle with?

Which of those are the most troubling?

Remember

Confusion, disorientation and roller-coaster emotions characterize a "normal" grief experience. No matter what you are feeling, be sure to tell God. Get in the habit of sharing openly with Him.

Talking to God

God, I think I'm going crazy. I'm having trouble making what used to be simple decisions, and my emotions are all over the place. I feel like this has been going on forever, and now I'm hearing on the videos that it will take longer than I thought. I need Your strength to make it.

In Your Life

Give an example of something you have done at home or work that shows a sense of disorientation or confusion.

How are your emotions like a roller coaster?

Responding to temptation

God's Word to You

"Then Jesus was led by the Spirit into the desert to be tempted by the devil. After fasting forty days and forty nights, he was hungry. The tempter came to him and said, 'If you are the Son of God, tell these stones to become bread.' Jesus answered, 'It is written: "Man does not live on bread alone, but on every word that comes from the mouth of God."'" (Matthew 4:1–4)

Why did the tempter (Satan) wait until Jesus completed His fast to tempt Him?

Jesus responded by quoting God's Word (the Bible) and applying it to the situation. What changes would you need to make in your life to be able to respond to temptation as Jesus did?

Remember

Satan tempted Jesus when He was weak, but Jesus knew that it is when we are at our weakest that God's strength can flow through. Instead of asking God to take away the suffering, Jesus trusted that God would be faithful to sustain Him through it.

Talking to God

God, it's a struggle just to make it through the day. I don't feel like fighting temptation. But giving in to it won't make things any better, or bring honor to You. When I am tempted, give me the strength to recall the truth of Your Word.

In Your Life

Check the temptations you've had related to your grief. Then add your own to the list.

❏ to give up

❏ to get in your car and keep driving

❏ to hide under the covers and never come out

❏ to be afraid of the future

❏ to quit your job

❏ to scream at ignorant people who don't understand what you're going through

❏ to injure the person whose actions contributed to your loved one's death

❏ to blame or doubt God

❏ to envy others

❏ to not care about anyone again—including yourself

❏ to take drugs or alcohol

❏ to work too much

❏ to engage in sex outside of marriage

❏ [list other temptations] _____

Satan will try to deceive you into using your pain as an excuse to sin. Pray for the strength to respond as Christ Jesus did.

He heals the brokenhearted

DAY 3

God's Word to You

"[The Lord] heals the brokenhearted and binds up their wounds."
(Psalm 147:3)

Who is the only One who can heal a heart shattered in a million pieces?

The above verse is a promise from God. What does this tell you about God's love for you?

Why is the "Great Physician" a good name for God?

Remember

Sometimes you have to walk by faith and not based on what you see or feel. While it may seem that God is content to let you writhe in pain, He is the healer of the brokenhearted, and He will bind up your wounds, if you let Him.

Talking to God

Lord God, I'm broken inside. No one can fix me but You.

In Your Life

If you had a broken bone, what steps would you take to help it heal?

What similar steps could you apply to the brokenness of your life as a result of grief?

Give God your burdens

DAY 4

God's Word to You

"Cast all your anxiety on him because he cares for you." (1 Peter 5:7)

"Do not be anxious about anything, but in everything, by prayer and petition, with thanksgiving, present your requests to God. And the peace of God, which transcends all understanding, will guard your hearts and your minds in Christ Jesus." (Philippians 4:6–7)

Praying (talking to God) is a great way to lessen your anxiety. On a scale of 1 to 10, rate how consistently you take your anxieties to God in prayer (1 being never, and 10 being almost all the time): **1 2 3 4 5 6 7 8 9 10**

Looking at your response to the previous question and the verses above, what conclusions can you draw concerning the level of anxiety you experience and the consistency of your prayer life?

Remember

God loves you so much. He is listening to every word you say, even when you don't feel He's there. Trust Him with whatever is troubling you.

When you stay in touch with God, you can make it through anything.

Talking to God

God, sometimes it feels like You aren't listening. But Your Word tells me otherwise. Help me to remember that You care for me and never tire of my complaints. Give me the strength to cry out to You for help and the wisdom to know that You are listening.

In Your Life

Hope does not come from things getting better, but from getting to know Christ Jesus better. Explain how this is true.*

* If you are unsure of how to answer this question, see The Foundation for Healing section of your workbook on page xi.

God wants you to tell Him everything that is bothering you. List below the things you need to talk to Him about. Then, take time to talk to God about those things.

Feelings vs. truth

God's Word to You
"Trust in the LORD with all your heart and lean not on your own understanding." (Proverbs 3:5)

What is the difference between putting your faith in God and putting your faith in your feelings?

What would happen if every person in our society or world made decisions based on his or her feelings instead of based on the truth of God's Word found in the Bible?

Remember
Put your faith in God's unchanging truth, not on your feelings, which change as quickly as the situations around you change.

Talking to God
Lord, as real and as strong as my emotions are, help me remember that what You say in Your Word is what is true. Help me to not fall into the trap of letting my feelings paint a false picture of who You really are or what You intend for me.

In Your Life
How can feelings lead you away from the truth of who God is?

What practical steps can you take to daily remind yourself of the promises and truths found in God's Word (the Bible)?

MY WEEKLY JOURNAL

The Effects of Grief

1. The loss of a loved one results in layers of losses that are uncovered as you travel your grief journey; for instance, the loss of dreams, relationships, possessions, time, duties and around-the-house helps (such as cook, mechanic or gardener).

The newest loss I have felt is …

The most significant losses I have experienced are …

2. Personal evaluation: How are you feeling this week?

	Really Bad	Okay	Pretty Good	Great
Emotionally				
Physically				
Spiritually				
Relationally				

3. Choose one (or more) of the following ideas to journal on:

a. Read this promise, and write a response to God: "Come to me, all you who are weary and burdened, and I will give you rest." (Matthew 11:28)

b. Whom are you angry with and why?

c. Describe some unhealthy things you do (or have done) in an attempt to relieve your pain.

d. What are some healthy things you could do to help relieve your pain?

e. When, or with whom, do you pretend that your grief does not hurt as much as it does? Why do you do this?

We encourage you to use a separate notebook for your weekly journaling.

WHEN YOUR SPOUSE DIES

T HE DEATH OF A SPOUSE IS PAINFUL. WHETHER IT'S EATING BREAKFAST ALONE OR GETTING INTO AN EMPTY BED AT NIGHT, EACH MOMENT OF YOUR DAY FINDS A WAY TO REMIND YOU THAT YOU'RE ALONE AND LIFE WILL NEVER BE THE SAME.

This session is designed to help you understand what to expect after losing a spouse and offers advice on how to navigate your new reality. By the end of this session, you'll hear answers to the following questions:

- Where is God in all this?
- Why do I feel so alone?
- Now that I'm a widow/widower, how should I deal with friends who are uncomfortable with me?

EXPECT GOD TO SHOW YOU HOW TO TAKE THE RISKS NECESSARY TO LIVE WITHOUT YOUR SPOUSE.

Video Outline
Use this outline to write down important concepts, encouraging words or questions you may have while viewing the video.

Why Does It Hurt So Much?
Your hopes and dreams died

> "YOU DON'T APPRECIATE THE HEIGHTS UNTIL YOU GO THROUGH THE VALLEYS." —EMY

Loneliness is your only companion

Friends leave you behind

You may have financial challenges

Advice on Moving Forward
You will have to take risks

"YOU CAN'T GO THROUGH
YOUR GRIEF IF YOU AREN'T
WILLING TO TAKE A RISK."
—DR. ROBERT C. DE VRIES

Fear and faith have a lot in common

Realize that you must adjust to your new reality

How to Adjust to Your New Reality
Realize you aren't betraying your spouse

Discover your new identity

"YOU NEED TO
ACCEPT HELP
FROM THE PEOPLE
AROUND YOU."
—LOIS M. RABEY

You must accept the fact that you are single

Embrace your new responsibilities

Managing Money in Your New Reality
It can be hard to make ends meet

It can be overwhelming

Seek advice from multiple counselors

Avoid quick decisions

Ask God for help

> "THE LORD JUST PROVED HIMSELF SO FAITHFUL. ONE OF THE THINGS THAT I'VE LEARNED IS THAT GOD HAS ALL THE RESOURCES WE NEED."—JODIE

Don't feel guilty about having wealth

You are a steward of God's resources

Remember God is your provider

Learn to distinguish between needs and wants

> "YOU NEED TO REALIZE YOU CAN EXIST WITHOUT ANOTHER PERSON."
> —H. NORMAN WRIGHT

Relationships in Your New Reality
The nature of your friendships will change

Set priorities and boundaries

You must make new friends

Dating and remarriage

Make sure you're ready

Signs that you're not ready

Remember you're emotionally vulnerable

Satisfying Sexual Desires in Your New Reality
What does the Bible say?

Unless you remarry, sex is not an option

You will have to make sacrifices

IN OUR NEXT SESSION
Your Family and Grief

Next time you'll look at how your family and friends are handling their grief and what you can do to help, while still finding help for yourself.

VIEWING THE VIDEOS MAY HAVE STIRRED UP STRONG EMOTIONS IN YOU THIS WEEK, BUT THE TESTIMONIES OF THOSE WHO'VE GONE THROUGH GRIEF BEFORE YOU CAN BE BOTH STRENGTHENING AND COMFORTING.

Through the workbook and journaling exercises, be reminded of …

- who will enable you to make it from one day to the next
- who truly understands pain as intense as yours
- who will take your burdens and meet your needs
- who is available for you 24/7

Before beginning each day's exercise, pray that God will strengthen you and give you the wisdom to accept His offers of help and provision. We also encourage you to use the weekly Care Cards in the back of your workbook.

He will sustain you through your grief

God's Word to You

"The LORD watches over the alien and sustains the fatherless and the widow, but he frustrates the ways of the wicked." (Psalm 146:9)

Whom does this passage say God sustains?

The word "sustain" has a depth of meaning. According to the definitions below, in what ways would you like God to sustain you? (Each time you check a box, say a prayer to God thanking Him that He will provide this for you.)

- ☐ to give support or relief to
- ☐ to supply with sustenance; nourish
- ☐ to keep up; prolong
- ☐ to support the weight of
- ☐ to carry or withstand (a weight or pressure)
- ☐ to buoy up
- ☐ to bear up under
- ☐ to suffer; undergo

Remember
God bears the burdens of those who are most in need of His help.

Talking to God
God, thank you for supporting me and, at times, carrying me. The next time I begin to worry about how my needs will be met, help me to remember that You will sustain me. Thank you for the relief that You give when I need it most.

In Your Life
According to Psalm 146:9 (see previous page), what should you remind yourself of when you begin to think/feel no one is aware of or understands your situation?

God often uses other people to help supply your needs. List three needs that family members, friends, your church or people in your GriefShare group could help you with.

Have you considered asking for help in these areas?

God is your source of comfort for deep pain and feelings of emptiness

God's Word to You
"If two lie down together, they will keep warm. But how can one keep warm alone?" (Ecclesiastes 4:11)

What physical needs do you have?

What emotional needs do you have?

In what ways are you feeling spiritually empty?

Remember
God not only understands the pain of your spiritual voids, but also your emotional and physical emptiness. Isolating yourself may cause you to miss out on God's provision of comfort from others.

Talking to God
God, most of the people who comfort me have no idea what I am going through. Give me the strength to be patient with them and not put too high of expectations on them. Since You are the source of comfort, please guide me to people who can help me.

In Your Life
Who has disappointed you with the amount of comfort he or she has been able to give you?

Make a list of what you were expecting from this person.

Once you are done with the list, spend time taking what you listed to God. Ask Him to comfort you in those areas or connect you with someone who can.

The power of prayer

God's Word to You
"Is any one of you in trouble? He should pray." (James 5:13)

When troubles hit you, how do you respond?

If you typically respond to troubles without praying, what can you do to remind yourself to follow God's directive instead?

Remember
God answers prayer.

Talking to God
God, help me remember to pray first whenever I am in trouble. Give me a greater awareness of how my different losses are affecting me. Give me the wisdom to enlist Your help every step of my grief journey.

In Your Life
How does it help you to talk to God?

Describe how you feel after you talk to God.

What troubles do you have that you haven't asked God to help you with?

He loves you 24/7

God's Word to You
"By day the LORD directs his love, at night his song is with me—a prayer to the God of my life." (Psalm 42:8)

The Scripture above is described as a prayer. Rewrite this verse in your own words to make it a personal prayer from you to God.

Remember
All day long, God directs His affection in your direction. At night, if you are lonely and afraid, sing and pray to Him to experience His comfort and protection.

Talking to God
God, thank you for loving me at all times—especially the times when I miss my loved one the most. You are always willing to listen to my cries.

In Your Life
When do you feel most afraid or lonely?

If you are fearful, what are you afraid of?

If you are lonely, what do you miss the most about your loved one?

Testimony of others who have been through grief

God's Word to You
"We give thanks to you, O God, we give thanks, for your Name is near; men tell of your wonderful deeds." (Psalm 75:1)

How has hearing the testimonies of other grieving people encouraged you?

What can you thank God for today?

Remember

If you think that your situation is hopeless, remember the testimonies of others who have made it through grief with the Lord's help. Give Him thanks for His proven goodness.

Talking to God

Lord, when I watch the GriefShare videos, I see how You have comforted and provided for so many people. I want to stand among those who "tell of Your wonderful deeds."

In Your Life

To date, which person or story on the GriefShare videos have you most identified with? Why?

What good thing has God done for you that you could tell another bereaved person about?

MY WEEKLY JOURNAL

When Your Spouse Dies

1. The loss of a loved one results in layers of losses that are uncovered as you travel your grief journey; for instance, the loss of dreams, relationships, possessions, time, duties and around-the-house helps (such as cook, mechanic or gardener).

The newest loss I have felt is …

The most significant losses I have experienced are …

2. Personal evaluation: How are you feeling this week?

	Really Bad	Okay	Pretty Good	Great
Emotionally				
Physically				
Spiritually				
Relationally				

3. Choose one (or more) of the following ideas to journal on:

a. Describe some hopes and dreams you had for the future that are no longer possible.

b. Describe your financial situation and what you are doing about it. How has God provided for you?

c. Which of your relationships have changed since the loss of your loved one? Describe the changes.

d. Where is God in your loneliness? Write a letter to God telling Him about your struggles with loneliness.

e. Describe a time when you felt naïve or taken advantage of when trying to do something that your spouse typically handled.

We encourage you to use a separate notebook for your weekly journaling.

GriefShare
devotional book

Available at local
bookstores, online
bookstores and directly
from GriefShare at
www.griefshare.org.

GriefShare CDs &
Downloadable Audio Files

Take GriefShare with you

Listen to GriefShare in your
car, at home or wherever you
go. Catch up on sessions you
missed or listen to your favorite
sessions again. You'll receive the
audio tracks from each of the
13 GriefShare sessions. Order at
www.griefshare.org.

YOUR FAMILY AND GRIEF

Losing a family member can be the catalyst for a family to grow closer together, or fall apart. This session's components will help you understand why, in order to keep your family together, you must remember that everyone grieves differently. This session will also show you where you can find the strength to make it through your grief without neglecting your family. As you watch the video, discuss what you've seen and complete your workbook exercises, here are some other questions you'll find the answers to:

- What kind of behavior should I expect from my grieving child?
- How can I tell if my family is positively handling grief?
- My child died. Is he or she in heaven?

> EXPECT GOD TO SHOW YOU HOW TO BE SENSITIVE TO
> THE GRIEF OF YOUR FAMILY MEMBERS.

Video Outline
Use this outline to write down important concepts, encouraging words or questions you may have while viewing the video.

Common Issues Grieving Parents Face
Grieving the loss of unfulfilled dreams

> "I DON'T KNOW HOW
> YOU WOULD RECOVER
> FROM GRIEF WITHOUT
> JESUS CHRIST."
> —DR. JOSEPH STOWELL

Bitterness, anger and confusion

The loss of identity

The struggle to keep grief from becoming an identity

Wanting to be with your child

Wondering if a child is in heaven

Signs That Your Grief Is Consuming You

Grief and Your Marriage
Don't expect to grieve the same way your spouse does

Your sex life may be affected

Make sacrifices to help your spouse grieve

What to do if your spouse won't talk

How to Help Grieving Children
Realize children grieve differently from adults

Realize children will revisit grief

Acknowledge your child's grief

Use age-appropriate language

Lovingly address defiant behavior

Watch for suicidal tendencies

Be prepared to help a suicidal child

Watch GriefShare for Kids *(Talk to your leader about the possibility of viewing GriefShare for Kids)*

Grief and Your Family
Remember your family needs you

Signs that your family is grieving in a healthy manner

Don't hide your grief

Cry out to the Lord for strength

IN OUR NEXT SESSION
Why?

You'll discover how to find God's responses to your questions "Why?"

THE VIDEOS THIS WEEK HAVE REMINDED YOU TO CONSIDER HOW OTHERS AROUND YOU ARE HANDLING THEIR GRIEF AND WHAT YOU CAN DO TO HELP THEM, WHILE STILL FINDING HELP FOR YOURSELF.

Completing the weekly exercises will help you begin to …

- accept God's comfort
- better understand the differences in the ways you and your family grieve
- find ways to help your family in their grief
- accept support from others
- think about your own identity

The exercises and Weekly Journal will help you maintain and build the relationships you have with your family during this traumatic time.

Receiving God's comfort

God's Word to You

"My sorrow is beyond healing, My heart is faint within me! … Is there no balm in Gilead? Is there no physician there? … 'For I will restore you to health and I will heal you of your wounds,' declares the LORD." (Jeremiah 8:18, 22; 30:17 NASB)

You can probably relate to the above descriptions: "sorrow beyond healing" and a fainting heart. What other descriptive images can you use to describe how you are feeling?

What does the word "balm" mean to you?

Remember

God invites you to come to Him for help. He is faithful to provide you with His healing balm, Jesus Christ.

Talking to God

God, this pain is too much for me to bear. I thought You wanted to comfort me. Why haven't I sensed it yet? When will I feel better? Please be my healing balm.

In Your Life

During this experience of grief, how has God comforted you?

If you do not think you have experienced God's comfort yet, describe your current attitude toward Him. How might this attitude be affecting your ability to receive God's comfort?

Jesus offers Himself as the light in your darkness

God's Word to You

"Even the darkness will not be dark to you [God]; the night will shine like the day, for darkness is as light to you." (Psalm 139:12)

You may feel "in the dark" about so many things concerning your loss, but God clearly sees everything that is going on. Since God can see and is in control of your grief experience, why does it make sense to allow Him to guide you through your grief?

In what areas of your life are you trying to do things on your own, without God?

Remember

God does not offer a formula, a set of instructions or any expectations for your grief process. He offers Himself.

Invite Jesus to be the light that guides you through the darkness.

Talking to God

God, I did not realize how dark my life could be. Sometimes I can't see which way to go. Please shine Your light for me to follow one step at a time.

In Your Life

In terms of managing your grief, or the grief of your family members, what do you feel "in the dark" about?

Say or write a short prayer asking Jesus to guide you in helping your family find the comfort and healing found in a relationship with Him.*

* The Foundation for Healing section, page xi, explains how to have a relationship with Jesus Christ and the importance of such a relationship in healing from grief.

Family members grieve differently

God's Word to You

"God sets the lonely in families, he leads forth the prisoners with singing; but the rebellious live in a sun-scorched land." (Psalm 68:6)

You may feel distanced from or incapable of nurturing your family members. When, since your loss, have you seen God's hand in your relationships?

How have you possibly blocked God from working in your relationships?

Remember

Every person approaches grief with different upbringings, life experiences, personalities, coping mechanisms and beliefs. So you may grieve in an entirely different way than others in your family.

Don't let grief cloud your eyes to the good things in your life, such as your family. Yes, you have reasons to grieve, but you also have reasons to hope.

Talking to God
God, sometimes I get so frustrated with my family members. Other times I'm so drained that I don't seem to care about anyone or anything. I know You are a faithful God, faithful to love, care for and comfort me. Give me the strength to pass on Your support to those in my family I haven't been supporting.

In Your Life
How do you feel about the fact that other people in your family are showing their grief in ways different from you?

If you are having difficulties with certain relationships as a result of your different grieving styles, write a brief commitment here to remain faithful to that relationship regardless of your differences.

Support of Christian community

God's Word to You
"Two are better than one, because they have a good return for their work: If one falls down, his friend can help him up." (Ecclesiastes 4:9–10)

How has backing away from others increased your loneliness?

How often have you attended church since the death of your loved one? If you have gone less frequently than before, what are you giving up?

If you have not been active in a church, what are you missing?

Remember

God has given you the support of people in your church and community to help you meet your physical, emotional and spiritual needs. You must seek out and accept help.

Talking to God

God, I feel like no one truly understands my loneliness. I feel off balance and falling without the support of my lost loved one. But You have called me to be part of a community and to see life from a greater, eternal perspective. I have to get out there and accept the support that's available. Help me!

In Your Life

Name three people you know who have a particular talent, gift or area of expertise that you could use help in. Then write their talents next to their names.

Pray now that God will give you the courage to take action to call these people and accept their help.

Identity in Christ

God's Word to You

"I am the vine; you are the branches. If a man remains in me and I in him, he will bear much fruit; apart from me you can do nothing." (John 15:5)

What does it mean for a person to "bear fruit" in his or her life?

According to this verse, if a branch (or a person) does not remain connected to the vine (God), it can do nothing. Relative to your recovery from grief, what are the implications of this truth?

Remember

Your life is about more than your losses. When you remain connected to and centered on God, you will move forward. It is dangerous to let something other than God rule your heart.

Talking to God

God, before the death of my loved one, I was finding security in things other than You. I know I can't base my identity on things that can change in an instant. I want to center my life on You, the unchanging, sovereign God.

In Your Life

What is your life centered on today?

What was your life centered on before the death of your loved one?

Why is it dangerous to place your identity in something that can change?

What steps do you need to take to connect to "the vine"? If you are unsure, see The Foundation for Healing section on page xi.

Visit the GriefShare online bookstore at www.griefshare.org for helpful books on children and grief, such as *It's Okay to Cry* by H. Norman Wright and *Children and Grief* by Joey O'Connor. Also, ask your leader about the possibility of viewing the GriefShare for Kids DVD video.

MY WEEKLY JOURNAL

Your Family and Grief

1. The loss of a loved one results in layers of losses that are uncovered as you travel your grief journey; for instance, the loss of dreams, relationships, possessions, time, duties and around-the-house helps (such as cook, mechanic or gardener).

The newest loss I have felt is …

The most significant losses I have experienced are …

2. Personal evaluation: How are you feeling this week?

	Really Bad	Okay	Pretty Good	Great
Emotionally				
Physically				
Spiritually				
Relationally				

3. Choose one (or more) of the following ideas to journal on:

a. The thought of being organized can seem overwhelming, but setting priorities is an important part of managing your family in grief. List the most important things for you to focus your time and energy on.

b. What kind of a legacy will you pass on to the younger people in your family who are watching as you go through grief? What will they learn from you about life, death, eternity and God?

c. How has your relationship with your spouse changed, and what sacrifices do you both need to make to preserve your marriage?

d. God is the father of the fatherless and the husband of the widow. What does this mean to you?

e. If grief becomes your identity, it will hurt you. What is the difference between these statements: "I am a grieving person." "I am a child of the King of Kings and Lord of Lords who has provided everything that I need, and I'm grieving right now." Which statement will you declare?

We encourage you to use a separate notebook for your weekly journaling.

WHY?

I S GOD IGNORING YOU? YOU MAY FEEL HE IS. YOU WANT TO KNOW WHY HE'S TAKEN YOUR LOVED ONE, AND LOOKING THROUGH HIS WORD FOR ANSWERS DOESN'T HELP. OR DOES IT? THIS SESSION'S VIDEO, DISCUSSION AND WORKBOOK EXERCISES ARE DESIGNED TO HELP YOU DISCOVER GOD'S ANSWERS TO YOUR "WHY" QUESTIONS. WHILE HIS ANSWERS MAY NOT BE THE ONES YOU WANT, IF YOU'RE WILLING TO LISTEN, THEY WILL COMFORT YOU.

Here are some of the questions this session's components will help you find answers to:

- Why?
- Why doesn't the Bible seem to answer my questions?
- Is there any hope?

EXPECT GOD TO PROVIDE DIFFERENT, YET COMFORTING, ANSWERS TO YOUR QUESTIONS.

Video Outline
Use this outline to write down important concepts, encouraging words or questions you may have while viewing the video.

God's Story
It explains why people suffer and die

"ESSENTIALLY GOD IS SAYING, 'I WANT YOU TO THINK MY THOUGHTS NOW.'"
—DR. EDWARD T. WELCH

It's the key to understanding your situation

You live in the middle of it

Dealing with Unanswered Questions
God never promised to answer all your questions

> "WHEN YOU ASK 'WHY,' YOU ARE IN ESSENCE VALIDATING YOUR OWN HUMANNESS AND REALIZING YOU ARE NOT IN CONTROL."
> —DR. TIM CLINTON

It's okay to ask God questions

Why God doesn't answer all questions

Knowing why won't take away the pain

> "THE END OF THE STORY IS A PLACE WHERE THERE WILL BE NO MORE TEARS."
> —DR. EDWARD T. WELCH

Ask questions other than "Why?"

God Has a Question for You
How will you respond to His story?

Will you believe in Christ?

> "GOD HAS COME IN THE PERSON OF JESUS CHRIST HIMSELF TO INTERVENE IN OUR PREDICAMENT AND TO BRING US TO A CERTAIN PLACE OF RESCUE AND A RELATIONSHIP WITH HIMSELF THAT LEADS TO HEAVEN."
> —DR. RICHARD BEWES

Why fix one problem, while ignoring the largest one?

IN OUR NEXT SESSION
The Uniqueness of Grief, pt. 1

Next time we'll discuss some of the factors that make your grief experience unique.

YOU SAW ON THE VIDEO THAT GOD'S STORY IS AN AMAZING STORY OF HOPE. IN THIS WEEK'S EXERCISES, YOU'LL BEGIN TO CONSIDER YOUR SITUATION IN LIGHT OF GOD'S GOOD AND ETERNAL PLAN.

By completing the exercises, you will start to …

- understand why people die
- think about the questions you really want to ask God
- consider what it means that God is good and whether you believe it

The Weekly Journal, too, will help clarify in your mind that a larger story is going on that involves good for both you and your loved one.

Why people die

God's Word to You

"Therefore, just as sin entered the world through one man [Adam], and death through sin, and in this way death came to all men, because all sinned." (Romans 5:12)

According to this passage, why do people die?

Does it seem fair to you that God would allow the sin of one man to affect your life? Why or why not?

It is important here to understand that this verse is saying that the process of death was introduced because of sin. It is NOT saying that the death of your loved one was the result of him or her being punished for a specific sin or sins. Remember, we are all human, we are all sinners, and as a result must ultimately face death.

All of us will eventually face God and be held accountable for our sins. Thankfully, God promises that, if you believe Jesus died for your sins, you'll experience His forgiveness. Make sure you've received God's forgiveness. See The Foundation for Healing section

in the front of this workbook for more information.

Remember
We die physical deaths because of Adam's sin. That's one of the reasons why the Bible says the wages, or the penalty, of sin is death (Romans 6:23). Thankfully, God makes it possible for you to escape eternal spiritual death by placing your faith in Jesus Christ.

Talking to God
God, knowing why people die doesn't make my loss hurt any less, but thank you for providing some answers to my questions. Help me understand how painful sin is to You if death is its consequence.

In Your Life
What thoughts do you have about your own death?

If this world is broken with sin, what hope do we have for the future?

God's answers to your questions

God's Word to You
"The secret things belong to the LORD our God, but the things revealed belong to us and to our children forever, that we may follow all the words of this law." (Deuteronomy 29:29)

How does it help to know that God knows all the answers but carefully chooses which answers to withhold?

How will demanding responses to the questions God chooses not to answer hinder your healing?

Remember
There are some questions that we may never know the answers to. Trust that what God has revealed is enough.

Talking to God
God, I have so many questions. So many times I cry out "Why?" Help me to accept the answers I receive from You and trust You with the answers You withhold from me. May my life reflect the answers found in Your Word.

In Your Life
What questions do you have that you think you will never have the answers to?

If you had the answers to those questions, do you think you would hurt any less? Why or why not?

Everyone has troubles, but the Lord delivers us

God's Word to You
"A righteous man may have many troubles, but the LORD delivers him from them all." (Psalm 34:19)

Prior to your loved one's death, did you think that because you'd lived a good life, God would spare you from such a painful grief experience?

If so, how does this verse change your thinking?

If God does not promise to exempt righteous people from troubles, what does He promise?

Remember

God never promised you a pain-free life. But He does promise to provide relief from your suffering.

Talking to God

Lord God, I know I'm not the only one with problems and suffocating pain, but sometimes it's hard to see beyond the fog that surrounds my life. I'm glad that You never tire of my cries and complaints. Help me to embrace Your deliverance.

In Your Life

Name a person you know (or a person you have identified with on the videos) whom God has delivered from his or her troubles. (Note: You will recognize this person by his or her peace, forgiveness, trust and thankfulness in the midst or aftermath of great suffering.)

What can you learn from this person?

DAY 4

God brings good out of loss

God's Word to You

"Am I in the place of God? You intended to harm me, but God intended it for good to accomplish what is now being done, the saving of many lives." (Genesis 50:19–20)

When your loved one dies, you have a choice, to go down the path of bitterness and destruction to yourself and others, or to trust that God is good and knows what is best for all. What choice will you make?

How is God's perspective of your situation different from yours?

Remember
God is good, and He can take the broken pieces left in the wake of your tragedy and transform them into something good. Will you let Him?

Talking to God
God, help me to trust that You can bring something good out of my loss. Help me to remember that You know exactly where I am and what I am going through. Don't let me grieve as if You are powerless to transform my situation.

In Your Life
On a scale of 1 to 10, rate the level of your hope that God is going to bring something good out of your situation (1 being no hope, and 10 being completely hopeful):
1 2 3 4 5 6 7 8 9 10

How is it helpful to know that God knows where you are in your grief and that He has a plan and purpose for it?

What is good?

DAY 5

God's Word to You
"I want you to be wise about what is good." (Romans 16:19)

How might your definition of "good" differ from God's definition of the word?

What doubts do you have about the goodness of God?

What has prompted you to doubt His goodness?

Remember
God's greatest good for you is to become more like His Son, Jesus Christ. And since Jesus suffered a great deal, you should expect the same, believing that the lessons you gain through your suffering are for your eternal benefit.

Talking to God
Lord, enlarge my understanding of what is good. Help me to want what You want for me—my transformation. Help me to accept the difficulties of the journey as well as the goal itself. I can't do this on my own.

In Your Life
Many people have the wrong idea that a good God exists to make people feel good. What qualities are better for you than to just feel happy?

If your definition of what is good differs from God's, how will that affect your view of suffering?

MY WEEKLY JOURNAL

Why?

1. The loss of a loved one results in layers of losses that are uncovered as you travel your grief journey; for instance, the loss of dreams, relationships, possessions, time, duties and around-the-house helps (such as cook, mechanic or gardener).

The newest loss I have felt is …

The most significant losses I have experienced are …

2. Personal evaluation: How are you feeling this week?

	Really Bad	Okay	Pretty Good	Great
Emotionally				
Physically				
Spiritually				
Relationally				

3. Choose one (or more) of the following ideas to journal on:

a. What is God's story?

b. Why doesn't God answer all your questions? How do you feel about this?

c. What truths do you know about the One who allowed your loved one to die?

d. What reasons do you have for hope?

e. Learning the promises of God is a daily, deliberate choice. How can you ensure that you receive God's Word every day? (Think of practical ideas that fit your schedule and your personality.)

We encourage you to use a separate notebook for your weekly journaling.

GriefShare online ➡ www.griefshare.org

Find a GriefShare group

Have a friend or family member in another city who needs a GriefShare group?

Our online search engine helps you find the nearest group!

FREE daily email encouragement messages

Sign up for "A Season of Grief." Receive an uplifting email message each day for a year.

GriefShare online bookstore

Helpful grief recovery books at discount prices. Find books written by experts from the GriefShare DVDs and other professionals.

THE UNIQUENESS Part 1 OF GRIEF

Betty Liddle, a GriefShare leader in Pennsylvania says, "In any GriefShare group, if you've got 10 people, you've got 10 different ways of grieving." This session's video, discussion and workbook exercises will help you understand why that's true by explaining the factors that make grief a unique experience for everyone.

As you complete this session, here are just a few of the many questions you'll find answers to:

- What do I do if I don't grieve as long as others expect me to?
- I feel like I could have prevented the death of my loved one. What should I do?
- How will the type of death my loved one suffered affect my grief?

EXPECT GOD TO HELP YOU UNDERSTAND WHY YOU SHOULDN'T WRESTLE WITH "IF ONLY" OR "WHAT IF" QUESTIONS.

Video Outline
Use this outline to write down important concepts, encouraging words or questions you may have while viewing the video.

How an Anticipated Death Affects Grief
Your grief begins early

"IN A LONG-TERM ILLNESS, GRIEF REALLY STARTS THE DAY OF DIAGNOSIS."
—JUDITH BLORE

Your grief isn't easier

Your grief may be shorter than expected

How a Suicide Affects Grief
You will have pain and questions

Is my loved one in heaven?

You may struggle with anger

You may be ashamed

You may fear others' reactions

You may need to find someone to talk to

How a Murder Affects Grief
You will face complex issues

Possible frustration with judicial system

You may have to wait for justice

How Accidents and Negligence Affect Grief
You may struggle with anger and frustration

You'll need to forgive

How Guilt Affects Your Grief
You may second-guess yourself

You may ask "What if" questions

How to Deal with Guilt Feelings
Decide if guilt is true or false

You can't forgive yourself

Remember, God determines how long we live

Refusing joy isn't the answer

How a Parent's Death Affects Grief
You may feel abandoned

How a Sibling's Death Affects Grief
Your grief may be marginalized

"CONDEMNATION WILL ALWAYS DRIVE YOU TO DESPAIR AND AWAY FROM GOD. CONVICTION WILL ALWAYS DRAW YOU TO JESUS AND CLOSE TO GOD TO SEEK HIM."
—DR. JACK HAYFORD

"GOD KNOWS THE EXACT TIME THAT WE WILL DIE. THERE'S NOTHING YOU CAN DO TO EXTEND YOUR LIFE SPAN ONE-TENTH OF A SECOND." —ZIG ZIGLAR

IN OUR NEXT SESSION
The Uniqueness of Grief, pt. 2

We'll continue discussing factors that make your grief experience unique and personal.

YOU SAW ON THE VIDEO HOW EVERY PERSON'S LOSS IS UNIQUE AND, AS A RESULT, THE WAY EACH PERSON GRIEVES IS UNIQUE.

This week's exercises will help you with some specific issues you may be struggling with, such as …

- your grief looking different from others
- your grief taking a longer time (or shorter) than others
- guilt
- a desire for revenge or justice
- laughing or smiling when you feel you shouldn't be doing that yet

We encourage you to also take time this week to write in your Weekly Journal. Doing the exercises and journaling your thoughts will keep you moving forward in healing.

God understands your unique pain

God's Word to You
"O LORD, you have searched me and you know me. You know when I sit and when I rise; you perceive my thoughts from afar … [Y]ou are familiar with all my ways. Before a word is on my tongue you know it completely, O LORD." (Psalm 139:1–4)

What is your reaction to the understanding that God knows you so well?

How does God's knowledge of the intensity of your pain compare with what other people think/know about your pain?

What other people think/know: **What God knows:**

Remember

The intensity of your pain and the length of time you grieve depend on several factors:

- the type of relationship you had with the one you lost (i.e., parent, child, spouse, etc.)
- how close you were
- the manner of death of your loved one
- how strong a support system you have
- how well you deal with trials and conflicts
- the number and intensity of past losses and whether you've healed from them
- your relationship with the Lord

Talking to God

God, You understand me better than anyone. May I always feel free to express to You what's in my heart and mind. At the same time, help me to be honest with other people and to accept their assistance.

In Your Life

How are each of the factors listed in today's "Remember" section affecting your grief?

God's Word is a firm foundation

God's Word to You

"Therefore everyone who hears these words of mine and puts them into practice is like a wise man who built his house on the rock. The rain came down, the streams rose, and the winds blew and beat against that house; yet it did not fall, because it had its foundation on the rock." (Matthew 7:24–25)

Why is "building on the rock" a good description of applying Jesus' teachings?

What does this passage promise for those facing the harsh storms of life?

Remember
Apply Christ's Words to your grief, and your grief will not destroy you.

Talking to God
Lord, I'm drowning in sorrow; my emotions are raining all over the place; and the winds of daily pressures are beating against me. I can't keep a firm footing on my own. Thank you for Your immovable support to everyone who applies Your Word.

In Your Life
Name areas of your life where you tend to lean on your own strength to get things done.

A wise person relies on God's sufficiency rather than on self-sufficiency. Why is this statement true?

Feelings of guilt

God's Word to You
"All the days ordained for me were written in your book before one of them came to be." (Psalm 139:16)

This verse teaches us that God determines our life span before we are born! How does that fact cause you to rethink any guilt you feel for "causing" your loved one's death?

Read the previous verse again. In light of what it teaches about God numbering our days, what questions do you have for God about your loved one's death?

Remember

Don't assume responsibility for your loved one's death. Ultimately our lives are in the hands of God. Zig Ziglar says, "Psalm 139:16 clearly states that our life every day is measured, meaning simply, God knows the exact time that we will die. He knows when He's going to call us home. There's nothing you can do to extend your life span one-tenth of a second." No death is simply the result of circumstances, an accident or fate. This doesn't mean God wanted your loved one to die or is morally responsible for the death. It means the same God who loved you enough to die for you is in control.

How can a loving God be in control, yet your loved one still died? You may never fully understand that. But that's why, frequently and lovingly, the Bible reminds us that God's ways are too complex for us to understand. That's also why when we see chaos all around us, we should remind ourselves of God's ultimate demonstration of His love and concern for us, the cross upon which He died for our sins.

"Oh, how great are God's riches and wisdom and knowledge! How impossible it is for us to understand his decisions and his ways!" (Romans 11:33 NLT)

Talking to God

Lord, it's hard to accept that You determined how long my loved one would live. Help me to accept it and continue drawing near to You for comfort.

In Your Life

If you think your actions, or lack of action, were the cause of your loved one's death, how do you reconcile that with the reality that nothing is outside of God's control?

Look to the Lord for justice to be served

God's Word to You

"Do not take revenge, my friends, but leave room for God's wrath, for it is written: 'It is mine to avenge; I will repay,' says the Lord." (Romans 12:19)

Some people feel they have the "right" to get revenge or to demand justice. Why is this incorrect?

How do you know God will ensure that justice is served?

Remember

Wanting and getting revenge never leads to peace, and it does not honor the Lord or your lost loved one. Peace is found in time spent with Jesus.

If you are struggling with feelings of blame or wanting revenge, hand over your feelings to God each time those thoughts enter your mind and replace them with words, actions, mental pictures, songs or prayers that honor God.

Talking to God

Lord, sometimes my blame and anger fuel me, and I keep fanning the flames with more and more negative thoughts. Right now, I surrender my thoughts to You. Please take these angry, bitter feelings of blame and teach me to replace them with Your Word, with prayer, with time spent helping others and with remembrances of Your forgiveness.

In Your Life

What does blame or revenge accomplish?

Instead of occupying your time with blame or revenge, what could you do with your time that would honor your lost loved one and honor God?

Enjoying life again

God's Word to You

"Then maidens will dance and be glad, young men and old as well. I will turn their mourning into gladness; I will give them comfort and joy instead of sorrow." (Jeremiah 31:13)

After your loss, how did you feel when other people began to get back into the routines of their everyday lives—working, laughing, playing and living?

A healthy, godly progression of grief moves from mourning/sorrow to _____.

How can a person continue to grieve a loss, but also be joyful?

Remember

Smiling, laughing or experiencing moments of pleasure are part of the healing process. You are not being disloyal to your loved one. You are moving forward, and this is something to accept and to be grateful to God for.

Talking to God

God, sometimes I'm afraid that if I start to enjoy life, then it means I'm forgetting my loved one or that my love for him or her is lessening. I KNOW this isn't true. Thank you for giving me some moments of enjoyment, and help me to look for more of those moments!

In Your Life

Name three times this past week when you have smiled, laughed or found pleasure in something.

How does it make you feel to know you have found reasons for joy?

MY WEEKLY JOURNAL

The Uniqueness of Grief, pt. 1

1. The loss of a loved one results in layers of losses that are uncovered as you travel your grief journey; for instance, the loss of dreams, relationships, possessions, time, duties and around-the-house helps (such as cook, mechanic or gardener).

The newest loss I have felt is …

The most significant losses I have experienced are …

2. Personal evaluation: How are you feeling this week?

	Really Bad	Okay	Pretty Good	Great
Emotionally				
Physically				
Spiritually				
Relationally				

3. Choose one (or more) of the following ideas to journal on:

a. Even though your grief is unique, grief is a common experience, and you can receive support from other people. Others know the heart-wrenching pain of losing a loved one. Write about someone who is your greatest support right now and why.

b. Different people find different things to be comforting. What different things do you and your family members find comfort in?

c. Describe any feelings of guilt you may have. Think about what God would want you to do with those guilty feelings.

d. What has surprised you the most about your personal response to grief? What does this teach you about yourself?

e. How concerned are you that "justice is served" and why? What does God's Word say about this?

We encourage you to use a separate notebook for your weekly journaling.

THE UNIQUENESS Part 2 OF GRIEF

RELATIONSHIPS, PAST AND PRESENT, WILL HAVE AN EFFECT UPON YOUR GRIEF EXPERIENCE. USE THIS SESSION'S VIDEO, DISCUSSION TIME AND WORKBOOK EXERCISES TO HELP YOU BRING CLOSURE TO UNFINISHED BUSINESS WITH THE ONE YOU'VE LOST AND TO SHOW YOU HOW TO RESPOND TO THE INSENSITIVE TREATMENT AND COMMENTS OF OTHERS.

Completing this session will help you find answers to the following questions:

- I thought I forgave my loved one for what he or she did to me. Why do I still wrestle with bitterness?

- Now that my loved one is dead, how do I receive his or her forgiveness?

- How do I respond to the insensitive comments of those who are trying to comfort me?

EXPECT TO DISCOVER WHY CHRIST'S DEATH ON THE CROSS IS THE BASIS FOR MENDING ALL RELATIONSHIPS.

Video Outline
Use this outline to write down important concepts, encouraging words or questions you may have while viewing the video.

Grieving Conflicted Relationships
Reminiscing can be painful

"I HAVE A HEAVENLY FATHER WHO WILL FORGIVE ME."
—DR. JOHN TRENT

Expect to grieve differently

Look to God for healing

Regrets are common

Moving Past Guilt and Bitterness
God's forgiveness is key

Forgiveness
Death complicates it

"UNLESS YOU ARE WILLING TO FORGIVE, YOU WILL NOT BE HEALED." —KAY ARTHUR

The implications of unforgiveness

Your loved one can't forgive you

Perfected saints can't hold grudges

"IF WE DON'T FORGIVE, THAT MEANS WE ARE CARRYING RESENTMENT AND BITTERNESS." —H. NORMAN WRIGHT

It's a process

Dealing with Comforters
Expect to be offended

Many won't understand your pain

Some will misuse Scripture

Some friends will avoid you

Why Are People So Insensitive?
They've never grieved

They may be avoiding grief

Hurt people, hurt people

> "IF YOU'RE GOING THROUGH BEREAVEMENT, PEOPLE WILL SAY INSENSITIVE THINGS TO YOU." —DR. EDWARD T. WELCH

Responding to Poor Comforters
Have mercy on them

Forgive them

Evaluate your expectations
(Read the article on page 90 to see if you're expecting too much from your comforters)

Communicate with Comforters
Specify your needs

> "I HAD TO FORGIVE THEM TO MOVE ON ... TO CONTINUE TO ALLOW GOD TO HEAL ME." —NANCY

Say more than, "I'm fine"

Don't dump on people

Handling awkward situations

Make others walk on eggshells

Wait on others to do the right thing

Make others comfortable

IN OUR NEXT SESSION
God's Prescription for Grief

Learn why it's important to listen to what God has to say about pain and suffering.

FORGIVENESS, AS YOU SAW ON THE VIDEO, MAY NOT BE A SUBJECT YOU WANT TO THINK ABOUT. TAKE TIME TO DO THE EXERCISES AND JOURNAL THIS WEEK AND REFLECT ON WHAT FORGIVENESS ACTUALLY MEANS. YOU'LL BEGIN TO BE AWARE OF ...

- what forgiveness is and isn't
- how unforgiveness hurts you and those around you
- the fact that people trying to help you may need to be forgiven for words that have hurt you
- what God forgives you for

Ask God to help you to want what He wants.

What it means to forgive

God's Word to You
"Forgive as the Lord forgave you." (Colossians 3:13)

What has God forgiven you for?

Have you been spending more time focusing on God or on blame? If you are more focused on blame, why do you think this is?

Remember
As difficult as forgiveness can be (and it can seem impossible!), if you desire to get your heart right with God and to heal, you must accept God's forgiveness and forgive as God has forgiven you.

Forgiveness is ...

- canceling a debt
- a commitment
- obedience to God
- a choice
- a process
- allowing God's love to flow through you

If you can't bring yourself to forgive, talk to your GriefShare leader or your pastor. They can help you accept why you should.

Talking to God
God, I do not agree with what that person did, but that's not what forgiveness is. Forgiveness is choosing to let You rule my heart when it comes to this situation. Help me surrender this to You and learn what it truly means to forgive.

In Your Life
Whom do you need to forgive?

How is forgiveness a choice and not a feeling?

What choice do you need to make about forgiving?

What it means to withhold forgiveness

DAY 2

God's Word to You
"For if you forgive men when they sin against you, your heavenly Father will also forgive you. But if you do not forgive men their sins, your Father will not forgive your sins." (Matthew 6:14–15)

When does God withhold forgiveness from you?

Why is it not your place to demand that a person pay you back for wrongs committed against you?

Remember
Forgiveness frees you from a lifetime of bondage to a bitter and hardened heart.

Talking to God
God, I can't do this on my own. The decision to forgive is a daily struggle. But I choose to trust You to guide me through this process. I choose to do Your will.

In Your Life
What is keeping you from choosing to forgive someone?

What does refusing to forgive say about the state of your heart?

Forgive those who have hurt you in an attempt to comfort

God's Word to You
"Then Job replied: 'I have heard many things like these; miserable comforters are you all!'" (Job 16:1–2)

Describe an instance when someone said words that were hurtful to you in an attempt to comfort you.

What words or actions have you found comforting?

Remember

You will receive "advice" that is insensitive and hurtful. Although other people mean well, they often say the wrong thing.

Seek forgiveness from God for any resentment you are harboring against these people.

Talking to God

God, when I think back on some comments that have been said to me, I burn with frustration and hurt. But I want to get better, not worse, so I'm choosing to forgive. Help me stay committed to this process.

In Your Life

What guidance can you give your friends to help them avoid insensitive remarks?

Write the names below of people who have hurt you in an attempt to comfort you. Spend time in prayer for each person.

Receiving God's forgiveness

God's Word to You

"If we claim to be without sin, we deceive ourselves and the truth is not in us. If we confess our sins, he is faithful and just and will forgive us our sins and purify us from all unrighteousness." (1 John 1:8–9)

What character traits do you discover about God from this passage?

What action will you take in response to these verses?

Remember

Everyone is a sinner. And the penalty for sin is death—eternal death, eternal separation from God. God sent Jesus to die to pay the penalty for your sin so that you don't have to.

Believing Jesus died for you, and receiving the free gift of His righteousness in place of your sinfulness, is your only hope of escaping an eternity in separation from God in a place the Bible calls hell.

If you would like to receive His payment for your sin, let God know that you believe He died on the cross for you and that He has the right to direct your life. This is the only way you can deal with any sin against your loved one. Your loved one can't forgive you now, and even if he or she could, it is God's forgiveness you really need.

Talking to God

God, I am a sinner in need of Your forgiveness. Thank you for sending Jesus to pay for my sin and raising Him from the dead to overcome the power of sin and death. Without that, there's no way I could be forgiven or get over the guilt I feel. I receive Your gift of salvation and choose to entrust my life to You. Come into my life, and give me the strength to make it through this difficult time.

In Your Life

If you sincerely meant the words you prayed, God has forgiven every sin you have ever committed and will commit. What must you remember if you start to condemn yourself?

If you have surrendered control of your life to God, how will your day-to-day life be different now?

The Foundation for Healing on page xi provides further information about what it means to entrust your life to God.

God's forgiveness is a reminder of His love

DAY 5

God's Word to You

"Out of the depths I cry to you, O LORD; O Lord, hear my voice. Let your ears be attentive to my cry for mercy. If you, O LORD, kept a record of sins, O Lord, who could stand? But with you there is forgiveness." (Psalm 130:1–4)

How thorough is God's forgiveness? (See also Psalm 103:12.)

How does remembering God's forgiveness bring comfort when you are crying out from the depths?

Remember

If you've trusted Christ to pay for your sins, reflect upon the forgiveness you've experienced. It's a constant reminder of His unparalleled love for you.

Talking to God

God, I've ignored You, rejected You, shouted at You in anger and at times have wondered if You are truly good. Yet, here You are offering Your unfailing love and forgiveness. You love me so much. I can hardly believe it.

In Your Life

Do you feel that you deserve forgiveness from God? Why or why not?

Why does God offer forgiveness to you even when you don't feel you deserve it?

The Uniqueness of Grief, pt. 2

1. The loss of a loved one results in layers of losses that are uncovered as you travel your grief journey; for instance, the loss of dreams, relationships, possessions, time, duties and around-the-house helps (such as cook, mechanic or gardener).

The newest loss I have felt is …

The most significant losses I have experienced are …

2. Personal evaluation: How are you feeling this week?

	Really Bad	Okay	Pretty Good	Great
Emotionally				
Physically				
Spiritually				
Relationally				

3. Choose one (or more) of the following ideas to journal on:

a. Write a prayer to God explaining why you don't want to forgive someone and asking for His help.

b. How is unforgiveness harming you and those around you?

c. What concerns do you have about unfinished business between you and your loved one? Bring these concerns to God.

d. Write a letter to your friends explaining things they are doing that are hurtful and what would be helpful instead. (See tips on how to write a grief letter on page 23.)

e. If you have chosen to forgive someone, describe how this daily process has been going.

ARE YOU EXPECTING TOO MUCH FROM YOUR COMFORTERS?

RICK BILLINGSLEY'S STORY IN THIS WEEK'S VIDEO SHOWED THAT YOUR EXPECTATIONS OF YOUR COMFORTERS MAY BE TOO HIGH. HERE ARE THREE SIGNS YOU MAY BE EXPECTING TOO MUCH. IF THESE SIGNS ARE PRESENT IN YOUR LIFE, ASK YOURSELF THE QUESTIONS IN THE "CHECKING YOUR EXPECTATIONS" SECTION TO DETERMINE WHETHER YOUR EXPECTATIONS ARE REASONABLE.

Signs That Your Expectations of Your Comforters May Be Too High

Anger with your comforters – Anger is always the result of an evaluation you make about your behavior or the behavior of others. If you conclude that you've been offended or mistreated, you may respond with anger. But remember, becoming angry doesn't necessarily mean your anger is justified.

Just as you evaluate the behavior of others and draw conclusions about it, God evaluates your anger. He determines whether or not it is warranted. To help you determine if your anger with your comforters is justified, see if you have any of the expectations listed under "Checking Your Expectations."* If you do, there's a good chance you need to admit that your expectations were out of line and ask the person(s) you were angry with to forgive you.†

Isolating yourself from your comforters – Sometimes, isolating yourself from insensitive comforters is necessary. It allows you to tend to yourself without the interference of others. However, it's easy to go overboard with this.

If you've totally isolated yourself from someone, talk to your group leader or a pastor to see whether your reasons for doing so are valid. Also, if you're isolating yourself because someone has failed to measure up to one or more of the following expectations, lower your expectations and reconnect.

Would-be comforters avoid you – If people are avoiding you, it's probably because they don't know how to comfort you. As painful as that is, it's not uncommon for people to respond to your grief that way.

However, unreasonable expectations of your comforters is another reason people may distance themselves from you. Check the list of unwarranted expectations below to see if you could be the cause of your loneliness.

Checking Your Expectations

Ask yourself the following questions. If you can answer yes to any of them, you need to reset your expectations of those who comfort you.

Q   Do I expect perfection from those who comfort me?

- If you do, it's not fair. The Bible tells us no one is perfect. Your friends and family are bound to make insensitive comments, become impatient with you or worse. Extend the same forgiveness to them that God has extended to you.

Q   Do I expect my comforters to discern my emotional, spiritual and physical needs with no assistance from me?

- Your comforters aren't mind readers. If you don't tell them you want to be alone or that you want company, they will have to guess. Don't fault them if they get it wrong. Learn to express your needs to others. See the article on How to Write a Grief Letter on page 23.

Q   Do I expect people to neglect their own families, jobs, responsibilities and interests to help me make it through my season of grief?

- As much as people want to help you, they have obligations they must tend to. If your needs for comfort or assistance are not being met, communicate these needs to your comforters so they can find a way to help you.

Q   Do I expect my comforters to grieve the same way I do?

- Everyone grieves differently, so don't be surprised if those who comfort you don't seem as sad or as upset as you are. They are grieving in their own way.

They may even think that mourning in your presence will upset you. If you really want to understand the grief of your comforters, ask them how your loved one's death is affecting them.

Q Do I expect my comforters to grieve as long as I do?

■ Again, everyone grieves differently. Consequently, those who comfort you may heal from their grief before you do. This doesn't mean they didn't love your loved one, nor does it mean they expect you to have moved on from your grief.

Q Do I expect my comforters to place me at the center of attention at all times?

■ In all likelihood, for a time, your grief will make you the center of attention. While this treatment can be pleasant and comforting, don't expect it to continue. Over time, those who care for you will have to tend to other hurting people, or they may be in need of comfort themselves.

Q Do I expect my comforters to fill the voids in my life that only God can?

■ Complete healing from grief is only possible through a relationship with Jesus Christ. Don't expect others to be able to do what only God can. For information on how to enter into a relationship with Christ, see The Foundation for Healing on page xi.

Q Do I expect my comforters to know that my refrigerator and freezer are filled?

■ If you're tired of lasagna and meatloaf, write a grief letter to tell people what you do need. Maybe it's not food. It could be something as simple as taking the trash out for you, taking you to the library or helping you learn to balance a checkbook. Whatever you need, the point is this: make your needs known.

Q Do I expect my comforters to allow me to mistreat them?

■ Just because you're hurting doesn't give you the right to hurt others. If you do, don't be surprised if others let you know you're out of line. Take their reproof seriously. You don't want to compound your grief with the loss of another precious relationship.

Q Do I expect my comforters to remain silent if I engage in unhealthy or addictive behaviors to cope with my grief?

■ Just because something or someone is comforting to you doesn't mean it's beneficial to your healing. Expect those who are close to you to let you know if you are looking for help in the wrong places. To be on the safe side, it's a good idea to ask your comforters to let you know if they suspect that your attempts at receiving comfort are putting you at risk.

* Even if you conclude that your anger is justified, ultimately, as Christians, we cannot stay angry with anyone. We are commanded to forgive others the way that God has forgiven us.

† These insights on the roots of anger come from GriefShare expert Dr. David Powlison.

GriefShare
devotional book

Available at local bookstores, online bookstores and directly from GriefShare at **www.griefshare.org**.

GriefShare CDs & Downloadable Audio Files
Take GriefShare with you

Listen to GriefShare in your car, at home or wherever you go. Catch up on sessions you missed or listen to your favorite sessions again. You'll receive the audio tracks from each of the 13 GriefShare sessions. Order at **www.griefshare.org**.

SURVIVING THE HOLIDAYS WHEN YOU ARE GRIEVING

Visit our special website to find practical information about surviving the holidays while you grieve.

www.griefshare.org/holidays

GOD'S PRESCRIPTION FOR GRIEF

Session 9

Y OU'RE PROBABLY GETTING LOTS OF ADVICE FROM FRIENDS AND FAMILY ON HOW TO DEAL WITH YOUR GRIEF. IT'S LIKELY THAT SOME OF THE ADVICE IS CONTRADICTORY. HOW DO YOU KNOW WHAT TO DO? THE GOAL OF THIS SESSION'S COMPONENTS IS TO HELP YOU UNDERSTAND WHAT GOD PRESCRIBES FOR YOU AS YOU GRIEVE.

As you view the video, discuss this session with your group and complete the daily workbook exercises, the answers to the following questions will become more clear:

- Does God really want me to be honest about how I feel?
- How can I experience the deepest healing?
- Lately my thoughts are so negative. How is this affecting my grief experience?

> EXPECT GOD TO SHOW YOU THE WAY TO EXPERIENCE
> THE DEEPEST HEALING POSSIBLE.

Video Outline
Use this outline to write down important concepts, encouraging words or questions you may have while viewing the video.

God's Prescription for Grief
Listen selectively to counsel

Christians grieve differently from non-Christians

It provides deep healing

Be honest

It prevents getting stuck in denial

Complain to God, don't curse Him

What to do if you've cursed God

Receive God's comfort

Cry out to God

Remind yourself of the gospel

Realize you're an interpreter

Realize the power of interpretation

See suffering from His perspective

Don't deny your suffering

Wait for healing

> "THE BIBLICAL VIEW IS THAT WAITING IS NOT SO MUCH ABOUT WHEN I WILL GET WHAT I'M WAITING FOR, BUT WHAT I WILL BECOME AS I WAIT."
> —DR. PAUL DAVID TRIPP

Don't attempt self-rescue

Wait for heaven

What you become while you wait is most important

> "WHEN YOU SAY, 'OH GOD, HAVE MERCY,' IT'S MORE THAN A PRAYER; IT'S WORSHIP OF THE LIVING GOD."
> —DR. RAY PRITCHARD

Worship Him

The uniqueness of worship

Grief is a worship test

To benefit from it, you must take it

The Precondition for True Healing
A relationship with Jesus

Only Jesus can save you

Believe Jesus died for you

> "FOR GOD SO LOVED THE
> WORLD THAT HE GAVE HIS
> ONE AND ONLY SON, THAT
> WHOEVER BELIEVES IN HIM
> SHALL NOT PERISH BUT HAVE
> ETERNAL LIFE." —JOHN 3:16

> "JESUS ANSWERED, 'I AM THE
> WAY AND THE TRUTH AND
> THE LIFE. NO ONE COMES
> TO THE FATHER EXCEPT
> THROUGH ME.'" —JOHN 14:6

IN OUR NEXT SESSION
Stuck in Grief

Find out how to keep from getting stuck in grief.

ON THIS WEEK'S VIDEO YOU SAW GUIDELINES TO HELP YOU MOVE THROUGH THE GRIEF PROCESS. EVERYTHING YOU LEARN BY VIEWING THE VIDEOS AND COMPLETING THE EXERCISES AND WEEKLY JOURNAL WILL HELP YOU MAKE IT DAY BY DAY THROUGH YOUR GRIEF.

This week's exercises will help you begin to …

- be honest about your pain
- consider the difference between a Christian who grieves and a non-Christian in grief
- define what worship means in your life
- apply God's instructions to your grief

We encourage you to cry out to God for courage and strength as you persevere through this GriefShare commitment.

Honest about pain

God's Word to You
"I am feeble and utterly crushed; I groan in anguish of heart … For I am about to fall, and my pain is ever with me." (Psalm 38:8, 17)

David, the warrior king and author of this psalm, honestly expressed his inner emotions to God. Write a brief prayer to God telling Him how you really feel.

Remember
Being honest about your pain before God is an acknowledgement that He is there, He does care and He will respond to your needs. He always wants to hear from you.

If you do not know the words to pray, open a Bible to the book of Psalms, and follow the example of the psalmists. (Here are a few good psalms to use as a model to cry out to God: Psalm 17, 27, 42, 43, 61.)

Talking to God

God, sometimes I'm not even honest with myself about my pain. Help me to follow the biblical example of pouring out my emotions to You.

In Your Life

What happens when you push down your pain instead of honestly expressing it?

With whom have you been pretending that your pain is less than it is?

Seeing pain from God's perspective does not mean denying its reality

God's Word to You

"I tell you the truth, you will weep and mourn while the world rejoices. You will grieve, but your grief will turn to joy … Now is your time of grief, but I will see you again and you will rejoice, and no one will take away your joy." (John 16:20, 22)

Describe the level of your pain as it is today.

According to this passage, what can you be hopeful about?

Remember

Your pain is real. Accept and feel your pain, but don't let grief cloud your eyes to the fact that God is good and has a plan for eternity. Grieve with hope.

Talking to God

God, my anguish seems unbearable at times. Help me to remember that my time on earth is a miniscule speck compared to all of eternity. Teach me about the joy and hope of eternity spent with You.

In Your Life

How does it feel to be around other people who have not yet experienced the death of a loved one?

When have other people made you feel like your pain isn't real or that it should be lessening by now?

Christians should grieve differently from non-Christians

God's Word to You

"Brothers, we do not want you to be ignorant about those who fall asleep, or to grieve like the rest of men, who have no hope." (1 Thessalonians 4:13)

Why is it wrong to say that Christians should be happy all the time?

Why is it right to say that Christians have something to be hopeful about all the time?

Remember

A Christian acknowledges and experiences the pain of grief, but also has hope in the complete and unending joy that is to come.

Reasons for hope:

- God is sovereign: He has a plan for all of life; He sees the whole picture, even when we don't understand.
- Life is eternal, and, for the Christian, all suffering will come to an end.
- For the remainder of the journey, He offers Himself to you. Walk forward with a new purposefulness.

Talking to God
Lord, in You I always have a reason for hope. Please envelop me with this hope. I'm going to keep trusting that You are in control, even when my life feels like the pits.

In Your Life
What is the purpose of your life?

If you are a Christian, how is your grief different from people you know who are not Christians?*

* If you are not a Christian, but would like more information about how to become one, see The Foundation for Healing on page xi.

Worship

God's Word to You
"Come, let us bow down in worship, let us kneel before the LORD our Maker." (Psalm 95:6)

How would you define worship?

Remember

Worship is the soul's response to God, anytime you are truly aware of the heavenly Father. You may be turning to Him in need, with joy, with praise or with a broken heart.*

God calls us to worship Him.

Talking to God

God, I worship You alone. I may have tears pouring down my face, but I know that You are real and You are good.

In Your Life

What inspires you to worship God (music, silence, creation, etc.)?

Why is it good to worship with others?

* Idea inspired by GriefShare expert Dr. Ray Pritchard.

Be doers and not hearers of the Word

DAY 5

God's Word to You

"Do not merely listen to the word, and so deceive yourselves. Do what it says." (James 1:22)

What is your usual response when you read or hear a teaching from the Bible?

What can you do to ensure that you remember what the Bible says?

Whom are you deceiving if you hear God's Word but do not apply it to your life?

Remember
When you read or hear God's Word, you must believe it and receive it in order to enjoy its benefits.

Talking to God
Lord God, I want to not only listen to Your Word, but to live it. Please give me a greater faith in You.

In Your Life
What do you know is right to do that you are not doing?

What have you learned from GriefShare that you have put into practice?

Name someone you can ask to hold you accountable when you are struggling to remain faithful to God's teachings.

My Weekly Journal

God's Prescription for Grief

1. The loss of a loved one results in layers of losses that are uncovered as you travel your grief journey; for instance, the loss of dreams, relationships, possessions, time, duties and around-the-house helps (such as cook, mechanic or gardener).

The newest loss I have felt is …

The most significant losses I have experienced are …

2. Personal evaluation: How are you feeling this week?

	Really Bad	Okay	Pretty Good	Great
Emotionally				
Physically				
Spiritually				
Relationally				

3. Choose one (or more) of the following ideas to journal on:

a. Write a prayer to God, pouring out your honest feelings. Do not be afraid to tell Him your complaints and cry out to Him for help.

b. What are the most significant lessons you are learning through your grief?

c. Worship God in your journal.

d. Describe a situation where you have been tempted to try "self-rescue" instead of waiting on God's answer to your cry.

e. Take inventory of the ways God is blessing you during your grief. Think of your blessings as threads of goodness being woven in with the dark threads of your life's tapestry. When your life's tapestry is combined with God's larger, finished product, what will the pattern of the good threads show?

We encourage you to use a separate notebook for your weekly journaling.

GriefShare online ➡ www.griefshare.org

Find a GriefShare group

Have a friend or family member in another city who needs a GriefShare group?

Our online search engine helps you find the nearest group!

FREE daily email encouragement messages

Sign up for "A Season of Grief." Receive an uplifting email message each day for a year.

GriefShare online bookstore

Helpful grief recovery books at discount prices. Find books written by experts from the GriefShare DVDs and other professionals.

STUCK IN GRIEF

WHILE IT'S IMPORTANT TO GIVE YOURSELF PERMISSION TO GRIEVE, SOMETIMES YOU CAN GO TOO FAR. IRONICALLY, THIS WILL LEAD YOU TO GET STUCK IN YOUR GRIEF. THIS SESSION WILL HELP YOU DETERMINE IF YOU'RE STUCK IN GRIEF AND GIVE ADVICE ON HOW TO STAY ON THE PATH TO HEALING.

Answers to the following questions will become apparent as you complete the components of this session:

- Is it normal to have so many "bad days"?
- Have I grown too fond of the comfort and attention of others?
- How will anger with God affect my grief experience?

EXPECT GOD TO SHOW YOU HOW TO AVOID GETTING STUCK IN GRIEF.

Video Outline
Use this outline to write down important concepts, encouraging words or questions you may have while viewing the video.

Am I Stuck, or Just Grieving?
Bad days are normal

Ambushes of grief are normal

Keys to Getting Unstuck
Realize God doesn't move parked cars

Realize time doesn't heal all wounds

Let go of the spotlight

Reconnect with others

Pray the Psalms

Deal with your anger

Accept God's comfort

Learn to trust God

Ask "Was he/she more important than God?"

Ask "Why?"

Ask "Am I keeping the relationship alive?"

Remember, no one grieves perfectly

Remember God loves you

> "I DON'T THINK THERE'S A WAY TO DO GRIEF PERFECTLY … BUT THE GOSPEL IS NOT ABOUT DOING EVERYTHING PERFECTLY." —SUSAN LUTZ

Anger is not neutral

Anger is a judgment

Lies at the root of anger and bitterness toward God

Monitor your thinking

> "IF I BECOME ANGRY AT GOD BECAUSE SOMETHING TERRIBLE HAS HAPPENED, I'M BASICALLY SAYING THAT HAVING [MY LOVED ONE BACK] IS MY SUPREME GOOD AND GOD ONLY EXISTS TO BE THE ERRAND BOY TO GIVE ME WHAT I WANT, AND HE HASN'T DELIVERED." —DR. DAVID POWLISON

Realize thinking affects feelings

Tell yourself the truth

Realize behavior affects feelings

Monitor your behavior

Consider changing your routine

Realize you reap what you sow

Grief is not an identity

"A MAN REAPS WHAT HE SOWS.
THE ONE WHO SOWS TO PLEASE
HIS SINFUL NATURE, FROM THAT
NATURE WILL REAP DESTRUC-
TION; THE ONE WHO SOWS TO
PLEASE THE SPIRIT, FROM THE
SPIRIT WILL REAP ETERNAL LIFE.
LET US NOT BECOME WEARY
IN DOING GOOD, FOR AT THE
PROPER TIME WE WILL REAP A
HARVEST IF WE DO NOT GIVE UP."
—GALATIANS 6:7–9

IN OUR NEXT SESSION
Top Twenty Lessons of Grief, pt. 1

This next session will introduce some of the most significant grief lessons that can be learned.

THE VIDEOS HAVE LIKELY CAUSED YOU TO START THINKING ABOUT WHETHER OR NOT YOU MIGHT BE "STUCK" IN SOME ASPECT OF YOUR GRIEF. THIS WEEK'S EXERCISES WILL GIVE YOU THE OPPORTUNITY TO EXAMINE YOUR THOUGHTS AND WHAT IS PROMPTING THOSE THOUGHTS.

You'll have the opportunity to …

- figure out why you may be angry with God
- ask tough questions about your grief
- move away from self-pity
- monitor your thinking
- discover what healing looks like

With God's help, you can become unstuck. Keep taking one small step forward at a time, and don't let anyone rush you.

Angry with God

DAY 1

God's Word to You

Job was a man faithful to God who experienced the death of his children, the loss of his property and livelihood and then his health. At one point he questioned and complained to God, but then realized, with humble repentance, that his own view of the situation was limited and that God knows all things, sees all things and has a perfect plan.

God asked, "Who is this that obscures my counsel without knowledge?" Job humbly replied, "Surely I spoke of things I did not understand." (Job 42:3)

Are you willing to listen to what God has to say to you right now, or are you more interested in doing the talking? Why?

What lies have you told yourself about God (anything that is contrary to what is said about God in the Bible)?

What will it take for you to let go of those lies?

Remember

Anger with God is always the result of a conclusion that a perfect God has treated you unjustly and that you have the right or the knowledge to judge God's ways. Take your heartfelt anger and pain to the Lord, while holding on to the truths you know about Him. He is sovereign, faithful and trustworthy, and He has not wronged you.

Talking to God

God, I've been accusing You of things I know nothing about. You are God, and Your good plan and Your perfect ways are beyond my comprehension. Someday I may understand, but for now, I will trust You.

In Your Life

Rate your level of anger with God (1 being not angry, 10 being extremely angry):

1 2 3 4 5 6 7 8 9 10

Is your anger causing you to: (check the following that apply)

- ☐ not want to worship
- ☐ not want to go to church
- ☐ not want to read your Bible
- ☐ see people in your life not as comforters and supporters, but as interference
- ☐ reject the goodness of God
- ☐ close your ears to His voice

When your instinct is to hurl accusations at God, what should you do instead?

Asking tough questions about your grief

DAY 2

God's Word to You

"May my prayer come before you [God]; turn your ear to my cry.
For my soul is full of trouble and my life draws near the grave." (Psalm 88:2–3)

What is your soul full of?

Instead of questioning God, what can you ask yourself about your emotions and responses to grief?

Remember

Your responses in grief often reveal what's truly in your heart. Use your emotional reactions and the questions you ask yourself about them as doorways to examining your beliefs about God, life and your purpose or value.

God has committed Himself to you in love; He's not going to back away from you if you make less-than-perfect discoveries about yourself.

Talking to God

Lord, help me to discover what's truly in my heart, and if I don't like what I find, give me the resolve to confess my sins to You and let You enter into every part of my grief. I want to move forward in healing.

In Your Life

While searching your heart, have you discovered that the person you lost is more important to you than God?

Have your hopes and dreams been attached to physical things or spiritual things? How do you know?

Move away from self-pity

God's Word to You
"Give thanks in all circumstances, for this is God's will for you in Christ Jesus." (1 Thessalonians 5:18)

Some people mistakenly think this verse means to thank God for every circumstance. What is the difference between thanking God for everything and thanking God in everything?

How does thankfulness help bring a person out of self-pity?

Remember
Constant grumbling and bitterness is a sign of self-pity and an indication that you may be stuck in grief. Teach yourself through God's Word how to be thankful even in the midst of pain and darkness. Don't let self-pity rule your heart.

Talking to God
God, I know that my grief is making me blind to things that are good. Open my eyes to see things that are good and not have tunnel vision on the bad.

In Your Life
Name three things that you are thankful for.

Starting today, become more aware of the words you say and the thoughts you have. Number the following statements from 1 to 4 based on how much time you spend each day thinking or talking about the following (1 being the most amount of time, 4 being the least):

__ myself: my loss, my feelings, my pain, my energy level, my future, my worries
__ other people
__ my job
__ God and His promises

Monitor your thinking

DAY 4

God's Word to You
"We demolish arguments and every pretension that sets itself up against the knowledge of God, and we take captive every thought to make it obedient to Christ." (2 Corinthians 10:5)

Which response sounds more like you?

☐ I miss my loved one so much. I cannot possibly go on. It's the end of the world for me.

☐ I miss my loved one so much. I'm not sure how I'm going to be able to cope, and I don't even feel like coping, but with God's help I can make it through each day one painful step at a time.

What negative thoughts have been recurrent for you?

Based on 2 Corinthians 10:5, what should you do with thoughts about your situation that are contrary to God's truth?

Remember
Telling yourself the truth means acknowledging the pain, but also recognizing what God says about your situation.

When a negative thought comes into your mind, counter it with a truth found in

God's Word. Continue this practice until it becomes a habit to dispute mental lies with strong, solid, hope-filled truth.

Talking to God

Lord, it says in the Bible in Hebrews 4:12 that Your Word is "sharper than any double-edged sword" and that "it judges the thoughts and attitudes of the heart." That's powerful. There's no room for self-depreciating and bitter thoughts when I have Your Word to counter them with!

In Your Life

What connection is there between a person's thoughts and actions?

Practicing true, focused biblical thinking is powerful to help you control and transform your thought patterns. How can you make it a daily habit to remember what is truth?

Use Scriptures to paint a picture of your healing

DAY 5

God's Word to You

"May the God of hope fill you with all joy and peace as you trust in him, so that you may overflow with hope by the power of the Holy Spirit." (Romans 15:13)

How well does your life currently compare to the verse above?

According to Romans 15:13, what can you expect to be filled with as you trust in the God of hope?

Overflowing with hope is a work of the Holy Spirit. How is it an encouragement to know that it's not a state you reach in your own strength?

Remember

Instead of being discouraged when you read the Bible and thinking, "I'll never feel this way," you can say, "God, this isn't how I feel now, but I want to."

Talking to God

Lord, sometimes I read Bible verses that I can't relate to at all. But I pray that You will take those verses and write them on my heart so that they will become a future picture of my response to grief and to You.

In Your Life

What does a person who is stuck in grief look like?

Describe what you hope your healing will look like.

Stuck in Grief

1. The loss of a loved one results in layers of losses that are uncovered as you travel your grief journey; for instance, the loss of dreams, relationships, possessions, time, duties and around-the-house helps (such as cook, mechanic or gardener).

The newest loss I have felt is …

The most significant losses I have experienced are …

2. Personal evaluation: How are you feeling this week?

	Really Bad	Okay	Pretty Good	Great
Emotionally				
Physically				
Spiritually				
Relationally				

3. Choose one (or more) of the following ideas to journal on:

a. Ask yourself "Why" questions about what you are feeling, and continue to ask a "Why" question for each answer you provide. Use this exercise to find out what's truly at the core of your beliefs about God, life and your value and purpose.

b. Read Philippians 4:8 in the Bible. Write down some "Philippians 4:8 thoughts" from the past, the present and for the future.

c. Pour out your angry feelings to God. Tell Him what you are angry about and why. Then write down declarations of what you know to be true about God in the midst of these strong emotions.

d. Describe a time when you were "ambushed" by grief.

e. Tell God about your loneliness or your depression. Ask Him to fill the empty places within You. Also ask Him to give you the courage to accept help from people who are trying to be there for you.

We encourage you to use a separate notebook for your weekly journaling.

TOP TWENTY Part 1
LESSONS OF GRIEF

MANY WHO'VE TAKEN THE JOURNEY OF GRIEF HAVE LEARNED VALUABLE LESSONS ABOUT SURVIVING IT. THIS SESSION UNVEILS SOME OF THE MOST SIGNIFICANT GRIEF LESSONS THAT CAN BE LEARNED. IF YOU COMPLETE THIS SESSION'S COMPONENTS, YOU'LL UNCOVER ANSWERS TO THE FOLLOWING QUESTIONS:

- How can trying to be strong in my grief be a sign of weakness?
- Where can I go to find help?
- How is it that grief shows me what I really believe about God?

EXPECT GOD TO SHOW YOU WHAT YOU CAN LEARN FROM YOUR GRIEF.

Video Outline
Use this outline to write down important concepts, encouraging words or questions you may have while viewing the video.

Lesson #20: God Uses Suffering for Good

> "GOD NEVER WASTES OUR SORROWS."
> —DR. JOSEPH STOWELL

Lesson #19: Life Was Always Out of Control

> "SELF-SUFFICIENCY IS A TERRIBLE PLACE TO BE. WE NEED GOD."
> —DR. JOSEPH STOWELL

Lesson #18: Delusions of Strength Will Hurt You

Lesson #17: Enlisting Help Helps You Heal
Find help, or find yourself stuck

Write a grief letter *(See page 23 for instructions on how to write a grief letter and for sample letters)*

You must depend on God

Lesson #16: Pray, Pray, Pray

> "IT'S THROUGH DIALOGUING WITH HIM IN PRAYER THAT WE'RE GOING TO POUR OUT OUR HEARTS TO HIM AND ALLOW HIM TO SPEAK TO US IN THE MIDST OF ALL OF THAT." —JAYNE CLARK

Lesson #15: Let Go of the Spotlight

Lesson #14: To Heal, Begin Serving Others
Share the comfort you've received

> "PRAYER IS A PERSON GOING BEFORE THE LORD BEING VULNERABLE. BEING OPEN NOT ONLY TO TALK TO GOD BUT TO LISTEN TO GOD." —SABRINA D. BLACK

Your ability to serve will grow

Help others depend upon God

> "SOMETIMES THE BEST REMEDY FOR GRIEF IS FINDING SOME WAY TO TOUCH SOMEBODY ELSE'S LIFE." —DR. LARRY CRABB

Lesson #13: Grief Exposes Your Beliefs

Lesson #12: The Bible Is Essential for Healing
Internalize Scripture

How to make sense of what you read

> "EXPERIENCES OF GRIEF
> CHANGE EVERYBODY. THE
> QUESTION IS, ARE THE
> CHANGES GOOD OR BAD?"
> —DR. PAUL DAVID TRIPP

Lesson #11: Grief Teaches You What's Important

IN OUR NEXT SESSION
Top Twenty Lessons of Grief, pt. 2

You will continue to learn about grief's most significant lessons.

BY WATCHING THE VIDEOS, COMPLETING THE EXERCISES, JOURNALING AND USING THE CARE CARDS, YOU HAVE BEEN LEARNING ABOUT THE MANY LAYERS OF THE GRIEF PROCESS AND ABOUT THINGS THAT CONTRIBUTE TO YOUR GRIEF. YOU MIGHT BE AT THE POINT WHERE YOU CAN CONTINUE YOUR HEALING BY ...

- passing on the comfort you have received
- serving other people
- recognizing good that has happened as a result of suffering
- rethinking your priorities

Ask God to give you the wisdom and the opportunities to apply what you are learning.

Passing on the comfort you have received

God's Word to You

"Praise be to the God and Father of our Lord Jesus Christ, the Father of compassion and the God of all comfort, who comforts us in all our troubles, so that we can comfort those in any trouble with the comfort we ourselves have received from God." (2 Corinthians 1:3–4)

According to this passage, what is one reason that God has comforted you?

What is the difference between being a container of God's comfort and a conduit of God's comfort?

Remember

God is well acquainted with suffering, so the kind of comfort He provides is from One who has been there.

His provision of comfort is limitless. You don't have to keep it to yourself because there

is plenty to give away. In doing so, you will become more like Jesus and will gain a deeper capacity for love and healing.

Talking to God

God, I may not be a grief counselor, but I know what's helped me and what hasn't helped. Please give me the courage to share what I've learned with others in grief so they will depend on You for healing.

In Your Life

Describe a time when you have spoken to someone in grief (or another crisis) and shared words that were helpful to him or her.

Sometimes words are not what is needed. What actions of comfort can you pass on to another person?

How have your words or actions helped another person to depend more on God?

The benefit of serving others

God's Word to You

"Serve one another in love." (Galatians 5:13)

In the Bible, Jesus was continually serving other people. What was His motivation?

If you are not motivated to help other people, where can you get that motivation?

Remember

You are especially qualified to help others because you have an intimate understanding of deep emotions, trials and personal struggles. Other people will sense that about you and respond to your help more openly than they might to another person.

Talking to God

God, with Your enabling, I have something to offer people, even in the midst of my own pain. Show me who needs my help, my care and my energy.

In Your Life

What activities are you involved in that help other people?

What activities have you been thinking about doing that would help others?

How has helping other people helped you?

God uses suffering for good

DAY 3

God's Word to You

"And we know that in all things God works for the good of those who love him, who have been called according to his purpose." (Romans 8:28)

If God is working all things for your good, what do you think would be "good" about your situation?

Since you began GriefShare, how has your view of what is good changed?

How would you describe your level of love for God? (See John 14:21.)

What conditions have you placed on your love for Him?

Remember

The idea that God uses suffering for good is the testimony of many who've walked the journey of grief before you.

Great suffering and evils do occur in this fallen world, but God can turn every situation around for an even greater good. We may not see how a person's early death could be good for that person or for those left behind, but God knows the whole story, and we must trust Him in His great love to know what is best.

Talking to God

God, it doesn't feel right to even consider that good might come out of my loved one's death. But, this is where I'm limited in seeing the big picture. This is where I think I know what's going on, when really I don't. You are the one who can provide my loved one with joy beyond imagination, with laughter, love and eternal delight in You. You are the one who always wins over death. Help me understand that there is a bigger picture, a greater story of love, and our lives on earth are smaller than a pinprick compared to a glorious eternity with You. I must trust that You know what is best.

In Your Life

If you had to explain to someone what the eternal God's perspective of your loved one's death is, how would you explain it?

If you picture God as a sculptor and you as His medium, how is God shaping you to become more like His Son? What is He chipping away at, and what is He molding?

DAY 4

Grief teaches you what's important

God's Word to You

"Do not store up for yourselves treasures on earth, where moth and rust destroy, and where thieves break in and steal. But store up for yourselves treasures in heaven … For where your treasure is, there your heart will be also." (Matthew 6:19–21)

What things in your life will continue to exist in heaven?

What do you treasure more now than you did before your loved one's death?

What do you place less value on now?

Remember

When someone you love dies, you quickly learn what's important, and what's not. This can lead to positive changes in your life.

Talking to God

Lord, am I leaving You out of things I'm valuing in life? Do You have a part in everything I do, everything I use and every relationship I have? I understand now that what matters is eternity. May my daily life reflect this hope-filled understanding.

In Your Life

What are you doing with your time that is valuable for eternity?

What physical things of no eternal value can you use as tools to support or enrich things that do have eternal value?

Prayer

God's Word to You

"Do not be anxious about anything, but in everything, by prayer and petition, with thanksgiving, present your requests to God. And the peace of God, which transcends all understanding, will guard your hearts and your minds in Christ Jesus." (Philippians 4:6–7)

In spite of the uncertainties of your new reality, the passage above tells you it's possible to have a remarkable level of peace. Using this passage alone, how would you explain to a child how to experience the peace of God?

Which thoughts and anxieties does God want you to bring to Him in prayer?

Remember

Prayer is an essential part of your healing. Prayer brings you into the presence of God. Use prayer to let God know what you need, but keep in mind that prayer is not a one-way conversation.

Talking to God

God, help me. I have so many needs and fears, so much confusion and sadness. I just want to be in Your presence, talk to You and experience Your comfort. Help me to be able to hear what You are saying to me in Your Word, and thank you for caring about me.

In Your Life

When you pray, which of the following do you do?

- ☐ talk
- ☐ cry
- ☐ ask God for help
- ☐ thank God
- ☐ listen to God
- ☐ confess your sins to God

If you don't know what to pray, use God's Words in the Bible to guide your prayers. Open a Bible to the book of Psalms and try reading one of the following chapters aloud (Psalm 55, 57, 61, 121, 141). If the words do not apply, choose another one.

Top Twenty Lessons of Grief, pt. 1

1. The loss of a loved one results in layers of losses that are uncovered as you travel your grief journey; for instance, the loss of dreams, relationships, possessions, time, duties and around-the-house helps (such as cook, mechanic or gardener).

The newest loss I have felt is …

The most significant losses I have experienced are …

2. Personal evaluation: How are you feeling this week?

	Really Bad	Okay	Pretty Good	Great
Emotionally				
Physically				
Spiritually				
Relationally				

3. Choose one (or more) of the following ideas to journal on:

   a. Write about how you have found help in the church.

   b. What small things have you done to help other people since the loss of your loved one?

   c. Before the death of your loved one, you claimed to believe (and not believe) certain things. How have your beliefs changed or been tested?

   d. What thoughts do you have about why some prayers are not answered in the way you hoped them to be answered?

   e. Choose a chapter or passage in the Bible, read a portion at a time and then write your reactions to what you've read. Here are a few suggestions: James 1, Psalm 23, 2 Timothy 1, Psalm 139.

We encourage you to use a separate notebook for your weekly journaling.

TOP TWENTY Part 2
LESSONS OF GRIEF

EARNING FROM GRIEF IS PAINFUL. BUT THE LESSONS LEARNED ARE POWERFUL. THIS SESSION REVEALS THE TOP TEN LESSONS OF GRIEF. WHILE SOME OF THE LESSONS MAY BE HARD FOR YOU TO ACCEPT NOW, IN TIME YOU'LL UNDERSTAND THEIR VALUE.

Here are a few of the questions this session will address:

- Will knowing why my loved one died take away my pain?
- I'm nervous about going back to church again. What should I do?
- How can you say God is in control when, ever since my loved one died, my life has been out of control?

EXPECT GOD TO SHOW YOU HOW HE CAN BE IN CONTROL
WHILE YOUR LIFE IS UPSIDE DOWN.

Video Outline
Use this outline to write down important concepts, encouraging words or questions you may have while viewing the video.

Lesson #10: Knowing Why Won't Take Away Pain

Lesson #9: Ease Back into Church

Lesson #8: Your Thinking and Behavior Affect Your Feelings

Lesson #7: Your Joy Will Return

Lesson #6: Grief Isn't Your Biggest Problem

Lesson #5: God Is Good

Lesson #4: Time Doesn't Heal All Wounds

Lesson #3: God Uses Suffering to Help Us Grow

Lesson #2: Joy and Pain Can Coexist

Lesson #1: God Is Sovereign (in Control)

WHO IS GOD?

■ HE IS THE LIVING GOD.

■ HE IS THE ONE WHO MADE US FOR HIMSELF.

■ HE IS THE ONE WHO HAS HIM-SELF ENTERED INTO THE SUF-FERING AND BROKENNESS OF THE HUMAN CONDITION.

■ HE IS THE ONE WHO HAS BORNE DEATH FOR THINGS LIKE MY SPIRITUAL PROBLEMS: THAT I TAKE REFUGE IN THE WRONG PLACE AND THAT I GET FILLED WITH ANGER AT THINGS I DON'T LIKE.

■ HE IS MERCIFUL.

■ HE IS POWERFUL.

■ HE IS GOOD.

—DR. DAVID POWLISON

"THE CROSS IS AN EVIL THING, BUT IT IS, AT THE SAME TIME, THE BEST THING THAT EVER HAPPENED. BECAUSE IN THE CROSS, GOD WAS PROVIDING OUR FORGIVENESS AND OUR SALVATION."

—DR. PAUL DAVID TRIPP

IN OUR NEXT SESSION
Heaven

Discover what God has in store for you in heaven.

THROUGH THIS WEEK'S VIDEO YOU WERE INTRODUCED TO MORE
SIGNIFICANT LESSONS LEARNED IN GRIEF. THIS WEEK'S WORKBOOK
EXERCISES WILL HELP YOU BEGIN TO ...

- release control of your life to a sovereign God
- realize the amazing goodness of what Christ did for you on the cross
- recognize what it looks like for joy and pain to coexist in your life
- accept that suffering is an opportunity for growth

You have two weeks left of your GriefShare commitment. You might want to consider taking this class again. Each time you repeat the class, you will be at a different level in your healing, and you'll focus on new and different information.

God is sovereign (or in control)

God's Word to You
"But I trust in you, O LORD; I say, 'You are my God.' My times are in your hands." (Psalm 31:14–15)

Why is it okay that your deepest questions may not be answered?

Read the passage above again, this time more slowly. What do you find comforting about these verses?

Remember
The most important lesson you can learn in your grief is that God is sovereign. That means He is in control of everything—nothing happens that is not filtered through His hand. God's ways are incomprehensible and far more glorious than you could imagine.

Talking to God

God, I surrender my life to You—my pain, my sorrow, my questions, my anger. I'm so tired of trying to maintain control, when really I can't. I know that You are good, and I will trust You in all things.

In Your Life

Which areas of your life do you try to control?

How does it feel when you are experiencing a lack of control?

How do you feel knowing that you don't have to be in control, that God will take over for you?

We know God is good because He died for us

God's Word to You

"For God so loved the world that he gave his one and only Son, that whoever believes in him shall not perish but have eternal life." (John 3:16)

How is Jesus' sacrifice on the cross an example of the greatest goodness, the greatest love, a person can give to another?

If the death of your loved one ever leads you to question God's love, how could remembering John 3:16 remind you of His disposition toward you?

Remember

Jesus' sacrifice on the cross for us demonstrates that He is good and He always overcomes evil with good. God can take the bad things that happen, the bad decisions of people and the terrible consequences of those decisions, and turn them around to bring about good.

Talking to God

Jesus, Your death on the cross was the worst evil, and You overcame it with an even greater good. When I confess my sins to You and believe in the goodness of Your sacrifice on the cross, my grief won't disappear, but I know I'll be able to move forward. Your love for me is amazing.

In Your Life

Are you more likely to believe in the existence of God or the goodness of God? Why?

Do you believe that any good can come out of the bad things that have happened to you? Why or why not?

Grief isn't your biggest problem; sin is

God's Word to You

"All have sinned and fall short of the glory of God." (Romans 3:23)

"The wages of sin is death." (Romans 6:23)

Taken together, what are the implications of these two verses for you?

Remember

If you are not a Christian, it's critical to understand that as real and painful as your grief is, it isn't your biggest problem; your biggest problem is sin.

God created a perfect world, but mankind sinned. Because of that sin, eternal death is our destiny unless we acknowledge our sin and surrender our lives to Christ. He died to exempt people from paying the penalty of sin. If you believe He died for you, you will receive the free gift of eternal life.

In addition to receiving eternal life, trusting Christ to pay the penalty of your sin opens the door for you to experience the full comfort of God. It's the only way you can fully heal from your grief.

"The wages of sin is death, but the gift of God is eternal life in Christ Jesus our Lord." (Romans 6:23)

Talking to God
Lord, thank you for meeting my greatest need, my need for a Savior. I believe You died for me, and I accept Your gift of eternal life. There's no way I can heal from my grief without You. Please show me how to go on.

In Your Life
Are you hoping your outer circumstances will change, or that you'll experience inner change?

What has your grief exposed about your character or beliefs that you would consider negative?

Joy and pain can coexist

DAY 4

God's Word to You
"Praise be to the LORD, for he has heard my cry for mercy. The LORD is my strength and my shield; my heart trusts in him, and I am helped. My heart leaps for joy and I will give thanks to him in song." (Psalm 28:6–7)

When you have cried out to God in your pain, what has He provided you with?

What is your response to God's provisions for you?

What do you think is a sign of healing for a grieving person?

Remember

You may be thinking that the absence of pain is a sign of healing. Real healing is characterized by the presence of both joy and pain.

Talking to God

God, even when I'm experiencing a moment of thankfulness or the recognition of something good, my pain is still with me. I don't think my pain will ever fully go away, but that's okay, because I know You'll always be with me.

In Your Life

What does it look like for joy and pain to coexist in a person's life?

The Bible says in Nehemiah 8:10 that the "joy of the LORD is your strength." How does expressing joy and thankfulness to God strengthen you in your weakened state?

God uses suffering to help us grow

DAY 5

God's Word to You

"Consider it pure joy, my brothers, whenever you face trials of many kinds, because you know that the testing of your faith develops perseverance. Perseverance must finish its work so that you may be mature and complete, not lacking anything." (James 1:2–4)

This verse does not mean to be happy about what happened. What reasons does the passage above give for being joyful in the midst of trials?

Why do you think perseverance is such an important character trait?

Remember
In a fallen world, pain is a part of life. When it comes, express your confidence in God's ability to use your suffering for good, by being joyful about your inevitable character development.

Talking to God
Lord, this grief can make me bitter for the rest of my life or it can make me better. I choose to accept this suffering and be open to learn from it.

In Your Life
What good lessons has grief taught you?

About yourself:

About your life:

About people and relationships:

About spiritual things:

MY WEEKLY JOURNAL

Top Twenty Lessons of Grief, pt. 2

1. The loss of a loved one results in layers of losses that are uncovered as you travel your grief journey; for instance, the loss of dreams, relationships, possessions, time, duties and around-the-house helps (such as cook, mechanic or gardener).

The newest loss I have felt is …

The most significant losses I have experienced are …

2. Personal evaluation: How are you feeling this week?

	Really Bad	Okay	Pretty Good	Great
Emotionally				
Physically				
Spiritually				
Relationally				

3. Choose one (or more) of the following ideas to journal on:

a. Describe a time when you have laughed or smiled since the death of your loved one. How does it make you feel knowing that your joy will return?

b. When you look at the cross—the cross where Jesus was crucified to take on the punishment for our sins so that we might live forever with Him—you will see that out of horrific evil came the ultimate good. Have you had an experience of something good coming out of something bad? Talk about this experience.

c. God acknowledges, understands and grieves over your pain, but He sees your circumstances from an eternal viewpoint. What do you think God's perspective looks like?

d. If you have been purposely staying away from church, explain your reasons why in a letter to God. Then ask that He will help you ease back into church.

e. Dr. Joseph Stowell says, "Self-sufficiency is a terrible place to be because it is the worst deceit we can bring on ourselves. We need God." Explain how this is true for you.

HEAVEN

O NE ASSUMPTION THAT MAY HAVE MADE YOUR GRIEF DIFFICULT WAS THE BELIEF THAT LIFE ON EARTH WOULD BE PAIN-FREE. WHILE GRIEF TEACHES THAT THIS IS NOT THE CASE, YOU SHOULDN'T GIVE UP HOPE OF A PAIN-FREE EXISTENCE. THIS SESSION REMINDS YOU THAT GOD HAS PROMISED A BETTER PLACE FOR THOSE WHO TRUST IN CHRIST AS SAVIOR AND ENCOURAGES YOU TO CONSOLE YOURSELF WITH THAT HOPE.

Finishing this week's video, discussion time and workbook exercises will help you find answers to these questions:

- Will I ever see my loved one again?
- Will I be married to my spouse in heaven?
- How can thinking about heaven comfort me in my grief?

EXPECT GOD TO SHOW YOU HOW YOU CAN
MAKE HEAVEN YOUR HOME.

Video Outline
Use this outline to write down important concepts, encouraging words or questions you may have while viewing the video.

Is Your Loved One in Heaven?

"THERE'S A LONGING IN MY SOUL THAT REQUIRES ME TO LOOK UP." —DR. LARRY CRABB

Myths about Heaven and the Afterlife
Myth #1: Heaven does not exist

Myth #2: You will be married to your spouse

Myth #3: Purgatory

> "THIS WORLD IS NOT YOUR HOME." —ANNE GRAHAM LOTZ

Myth #4: Reincarnation

Myth #5: Your loved ones become angels

Why Is Heaven So Wonderful?
Nothing on earth compares

> "WHAT MAKES HEAVEN EXCITING TO ME IS BEING WITH THE LORD JESUS WHERE I WILL BE PERFECTLY AND UTTERLY AT HOME." —JONI EARECKSON TADA

You'll see your loved ones

You will see Jesus

Your loved ones are safe

> "I'M FAR BETTER OFF IN THE PRESENCE OF THE KING OF KINGS AND THE LORD OF LORDS, MY WONDERFUL SAVIOR, THAN I COULD EVER BE HERE ON PLANET EARTH." —DR. BILL BRIGHT

You Must Wait for Heaven
You will have pain in this life

You have reason for biblical hope

More Myths about Heaven

Heaven is home to all

Heaven is home to those who earn it

Glimpses of Heaven

"Miracle Moments"

WHAT'S NEXT?

If you're completing your first GriefShare group, think about participating in another cycle. You will be sure to learn new things because you will be at a different level of grieving. You can be a blessing to a first-time group member, and you'll enjoy the continued friendships of others who are also on the journey from mourning to joy.

GriefShare CDs &
Downloadable Audio Files
Take GriefShare with you
Listen to GriefShare in your car, at home or wherever you go. Catch up on sessions you missed or listen to your favorite sessions again. You'll receive the audio tracks from each of the 13 GriefShare sessions. Order at **www.griefshare.org**.

THE VIDEOS GAVE YOU A GLIMPSE OF WHAT YOU CAN LOOK FORWARD TO IN HEAVEN. COMPLETING THE EXERCISES WILL HELP YOU HAVE A MORE FOCUSED UNDERSTANDING OF THE FOLLOWING TOPICS:

- who goes to heaven
- what heaven will be like and what you will do there
- the effects of thinking about heaven
- living with an eternal perspective

Congratulations on completing the GriefShare program. Please consider attending another 13-week cycle to further aid your healing. You will also be better able to help other people who have begun the grief process.

Who goes to heaven?

God's Word to You
"Jesus said ... 'I am the resurrection and the life. He who believes in me will live, even though he dies; and whoever lives and believes in me will never die. Do you believe this?'" (John 11:25–26)

According to the Bible, who goes to heaven and will live forever?

What concerns do you have about your loved one's eternal dwelling place?

Do you believe that Jesus is the resurrection and the life?

Remember
If you are concerned that your loved one isn't in heaven, keep in mind that your loved one may have become a Christian without you knowing it. Simply coming to God in faith, believing Christ died on the cross for you, saves you from sin. In most cases, you don't know for sure what your loved one believed in his or her heart.

Talking to God
God, You want everyone to be saved, and You give us so many opportunities to accept Your free gift of eternal life. Thanks for never giving up on us.

In Your Life
What concerns do you have about your own eternal dwelling place?

How does a person know for sure that he or she is going to heaven?*

* If you would like further details about an eternal relationship with Christ, read The Foundation for Healing section on page xi.

The wonders of heaven

DAY 2

God's Word to You
"Come, you who are blessed by my Father; take your inheritance, the kingdom prepared for you since the creation of the world." (Matthew 25:34)

If you have given God control of your life, you are now His child, His heir. What is the inheritance that He promises you?

If God has spent that long preparing His kingdom for you, how awesome do you think this kingdom is going to be?

Remember

Heaven is far better than anything you can imagine on earth. The best thing about heaven is that Jesus Christ will be there. It may be hard for you to imagine how glorious and wonderful that will be. You will be completely satisfied to the deepest levels of your soul in heaven with Jesus Christ.

Talking to God

Thank you, God, for providing this incredible life for my loved ones and me! Please give me the strength to persevere until I get there.

In Your Life

Describe a moment in your life that brought you great joy.

Describe a time when you saw something extraordinarily beautiful.

Name some people whom you love dearly.

Consider these wonderful moments and people, and be assured that the glories of heaven are multiplied far beyond all these put together.

You won't be married, but you will know loved ones in heaven

God's Word to You

"At the resurrection people will neither marry nor be given in marriage; they will be like the angels in heaven." (Matthew 22:30)

What thoughts do you have about the fact that you won't be married in heaven?

When a person gets to heaven, why will it not matter to him or her that marriage as we know it does not exist?

Who will be at the core of all our relationships, and how will that affect our relationships?

Remember
Although the Bible says you won't be married in heaven, this will in no way detract from your joy. You will see and know your spouse and other people, and most importantly, you will know and be with Christ forever.

Talking to God
God, it will be phenomenal to see You and talk with You and be amazed by Your glory in heaven. I am also looking forward to deepening the friendships I have here on earth. We'll have eternity to get to know the most wonderful things about each other and You!

In Your Life
Whom are you looking forward to seeing in heaven?

Why does the Bible say you will be even more joyous about seeing Jesus in heaven than you will be about seeing your loved ones?

The benefits of thinking of heaven

DAY 4

God's Word to You
"Since, then, you have been raised with Christ, set your hearts on things above, where Christ is seated at the right hand of God. Set your minds on things above, not on earthly things." (Colossians 3:1–2)

How could thinking about heaven affect how you live today and every day?

Where can you learn more about heaven?

Remember
Heaven is real, and everyone on earth has the choice to go there. Nothing on earth compares with heaven. There will be no pain, no suffering, no hardships, no misunderstandings, no arguments, no injustice, no cruelty. Heaven is safe, problem-free and an absolute certainty.

Talking to God
God, Your promises are a sure thing. A person in heaven wouldn't even want to come back here. While I wait for my turn to be with You in heaven, help me to live purposefully and be devoted to doing Your work.

In Your Life
How much does your heavenly Father love you and your lost loved one?

What do you picture your loved one doing in heaven?

How is this comforting to you?

A proper perspective on trials and suffering

God's Word to You
"I consider that our present sufferings are not worth comparing with the glory that will be revealed in us." (Romans 8:18)

What is the limit of time on our present sufferings?

How much will heaven outshine anything bad that is happening now?

Remember
If you are trying to make sense of your suffering, you must put it in the larger context of eternity. Yes, you may be tired and sorrowful, but you can also be hopeful and trusting and walk forward in the peaceful reassurance of God's sovereign plan.

Talking to God
God, my spirit is longing for something more. Oh, how my heart aches sometimes. May I walk forward secure in the certainty of heaven's joy-filled existence and of my own eternal destination. And as I wait to go there, may I live my life always mindful of Your promises.*

In Your Life
What are your hopes and dreams attached to?

If you knew with certainty that you would see your loved one again someday, how would that change your grieving?

Write a brief prayer to God declaring what you know to be true about heaven.

* Remember, heaven is only home to those who have placed their faith in Jesus Christ. If you would like further details about an eternal relationship with Christ, read The Foundation for Healing section on page xi.

MY WEEKLY JOURNAL

Heaven

1. The loss of a loved one results in layers of losses that are uncovered as you travel your grief journey; for instance, the loss of dreams, relationships, possessions, time, duties and around-the-house helps (such as cook, mechanic or gardener).

The newest loss I have felt is …

The most significant losses I have experienced are …

2. Personal evaluation: How are you feeling this week?

	Really Bad	Okay	Pretty Good	Great
Emotionally				
Physically				
Spiritually				
Relationally				

3. Choose one (or more) of the following ideas to journal on:

a. How do thoughts of heaven help you endure daily difficulties?

b. What are you most looking forward to in heaven?

c. What have you been taught to believe about the afterlife? Have these beliefs undergone any changes? If yes, how so?

d. Tell God any doubts you have about heaven and ask for His help in clarifying your beliefs.

e. What does God promise you in this life before heaven?

We encourage you to use a separate notebook for your weekly journaling.

SURVIVING THE HOLIDAYS
WHEN YOU ARE GRIEVING

Visit our special website to find practical information about surviving the holidays while you grieve.

www.griefshare.org/holidays

NOTES FOR THE JOURNEY

NOTES FOR THE JOURNEY

NOTES FOR THE JOURNEY